YOUNG MARY STUART,
QUEEN OF SCOTS

YOUNG

J. B. LIPPINCOTT COMPANY

MARY STUART

Queen of Scots

BY MARIAN KING

PHILADELPHIA AND NEW YORK

Other books by the same author:

Author's Note

Uncounted hours have been spent not only in the writing of this volume but also in research for authentic background material. Rare books, documents, and state papers were consulted as well as the most recent publications on the subject. Thus from diversified sources I have attempted to gain a knowledge of the life and customs of the places and period in which Mary Stuart lived.

A mere listing of all books consulted would be tedious. The interested reader may find all the more important French and English sources listed in Conyers Read's *Bibliography of British History—Tudor Period, 1485-1603*. A selective listing is appended at the end of this volume.

Even though *Young Mary Stuart, Queen of Scots* is in story form, I have not put words in the mouths of any of the characters. Where conversations or letters are quoted, I have used my own judgment in omitting portions that seemed to have no immediate bearing on the incidents I relate. Quite often I have combined one or more letters having the same context and source.

I wish to take this opportunity to express my sincere appreciation for the valuable assistance and cooperation rendered me by Mr. Robert Haynes, Harvard College Library; Miss Mary Ethel Bubb, Assistant Coordinator of Children's Services and Mr. Phillip Stone, Chief of History Division, of the Public Library, Washington, D. C.; at the Library of Congress, Lt. Colonel Willard Webb, Stack and Reader Division, Mr. Thomas Shaw, Reference Department, Mr. Legare Obear and Mr. Ralph Henderson, Loan Division; Mr. Henry M. Fuller and Miss Barbara Simison of Yale University Library; Mr. Paul North Rice, New York Public Library; Mr. McGill James, Assistant Director of the National Gallery of Art; Miss Jessie Matson, the Metropolitan Museum of Art; Mr. Paul Gore-Booth, Director General of British Information Services in the United States, and Mrs. Janet Locke of the British Embassy Information Office; the Reverend George Docherty, D.D. of Washington, D. C.; Mr. G. H. Edgell, Director, Boston Museum of Fine Arts; Louis Clark Keating, Ph.D., and Mr. William Clubb, Department of Romance Languages, George Washington University; Mr. H. Carrington Lancaster, Ph.D., Department of Romance Languages, Johns Hopkins University; and the French Cultural Bureau in New York City.

A special expression of gratitude is due the following, each of whom has read the manuscript for its historical and cultural accuracy: Dean Elmer Louis Kayser of George Washington University; Bernerd Clarke Weber, Ph.D., History Department, University of Alabama; Mr. David E. Finley, Director, and Mr. Erwin O. Christensen, Curator, of the Index of American Design, at the National Gallery of Art.

To my friends overseas I am deeply grateful for their untiring efforts to supply much of the detailed research material: in Scotland, Sir Thomas Innes of Learney, Court of the Lord Lyon, The Reverend James Bulloch, B.D. and

Mr. R. E. Hutchinson, Assistant Keeper at the Scottish National Portrait Gallery; in England, Mr. F. G. Rendall and Mr. E. B. Oldman, Principal Keepers of the British Museum, and Sir Garrad Tyrhitt-Drake, Chairman of the Museum Committee, at Maidstone; and in France, Mr. A. Martin, Le Conservateur en chef du Départment des Imprimés du Bibliothèque Nationale.

I wish to thank the following booksellers for their magnificent services: John Grant Ltd., James Thin, of Edinburgh, and Francis Edwards Ltd. of London.

I am particularly grateful to Mr. Carl H. Claudy, not only for his time and constructive criticism while writing this book, but also for his cherished friendship over the years.

Marian King

Washington, D. C.

YOUNG MARY STUART, QUEEN OF SCOTS

Chapter One

At Dumbarton Castle in Scotland, young Mary Stuart, Queen of Scots, stood with her French mother, Mary of Guise, watching the small barges move between the vessels newly anchored in the River Clyde, below. Three large galleys and a smaller one rode high in the water. It was August 7, 1548.

The Queen Mother turned away. These were the ships which would soon carry Scotland's Queen to France. Mary of Guise begrudged each hour that was not spent with her child. Mary Stuart had been the center of her life for all the child's five and a half years. She had fought for her and cherished her. Now, for the sake of that child Queen, her mother must send her to another land. If only James V had lived, this daughter of theirs would not be going away without father or mother to comfort her.

Mary of Guise suppressed a sigh as her thoughts turned back to the day Mary Stuart was born at Linlithgow Palace. It had been the Friday of December 8, 1542. Twenty miles away, at Falkland Castle, the King had lain desperately ill, bemoaning his defeat by the armies of his uncle, Henry VIII of England. Six days later the thirty-year-old King had died.

Ever since Mary Stuart's hurried coronation when she was but nine months old, the child's life had been a flight from the English. War had resulted when the young Queen's representatives, who were Roman Catholic Scots, had refused Protestant Henry VIII's proposal that his sickly heir, Edward, should marry the young Scottish Queen. Mary Stuart's followers knew that such a betrothal would have meant not only the subjugation of Scotland but also the supremacy of Protestantism. Henry's vengeance for their refusal began in the spring of 1544. His armies invaded, going deep into the land, devastating the countryside, and pillaging as they went. Although the Scots fought valiantly, they were not strong enough. They had appealed to France for aid, yet even with French assistance they could not quell the English. Henry VIII's death in January of 1547 did not stop the invasion; Lord Protector Somerset carried on the same ruthless warfare in the name of his new sovereign, Edward VI.

Remembering, Mary of Guise shaded her eyes. The bright sunlight caught on each ripple of the river below and shone back at her. It was hard to believe that it was less than a year since the child Queen and her four little Lady Marys who were the young girl's companions and her age— Mary Beaton, Mary Seton, Mary Fleming, and Mary Livingston—had escaped during the night with Nurse Janet Sinclair, Governess Lady Fleming, and the Queen Mother, just ahead of Edward VI's armies. They had fled on horseback to the priory of Inchmahome on the Lake of Menteith. How happy and carefree the children had been on that island home! It had been a safe refuge.

Only a month ago, July 7, 1548, the French lieutenant general, Sieur d'Essé, had made known to Mary Stuart's parliament Henri II's desire that a marriage should be arranged between the Queen of Scots and the young Dauphin, François. In return for this, France offered to defend Scotland against her enemies. The French asked that Mary Stuart be sent to France at once, to insure her safety. Careful supervision would be given her formal and religious education, and full affection would be bestowed upon her. Mary Stuart's parliament had hurriedly sanctioned the French proposals on condition that Scotland retain her laws, customs, and freedom, as under her former kings.

Mary of Guise would stay behind to protect her daughter's heritage, as she had guarded it since James' death. It was almost unbelievable that she no longer would caress that lovely face with its dancing hazel eyes, or feel those small arms around her. Mary Stuart would not be a little girl when she saw her again. Would they be able to keep the devotion each now felt for the other?

The Queen Mother had been unable to tell her daughter of the impending separation. Mary Stuart knew of the arrival of the galleys—she had laughed heartily as her mother made a story of the way Admiral Villegaignon had skillfully evaded the prowling English ships. She knew she was going to France any day now, but she took it for granted her mother would go with her.

Mary of Guise realized that not a moment was being wasted in loading the ships. Each hour counted; even now spies probably were carrying the news to England. Mary Stuart must be told now that she would go to France without her mother.

Looking earnestly into the child's happy face the Queen Mother put her arm around Mary Stuart and drew her closer. Mary of Guise paused but a moment, then told her daughter that she would not sail with her but must remain in Scotland for a while to watch over Mary Stuart's kingdom. But as soon as possible she, too, would go to France. Meanwhile, Mary of Guise explained, she would write often. For her mother's sake Mary Stuart must stay happy. She hoped it would not be long before the two of them would walk together through the beautiful French gardens.

Mary Stuart tried hard not to cry. Her mother was proud of her. Yet it hurt to see the child struggle to control her emotions. To divert her, Mary of Guise pointed out Admiral Villegaignon and Sieur de Brézé giving orders to their sturdy, bronzed crews. The King had sent these brave and kind men to bring Mary Stuart to France. His Majesty had even sent his own galley! It was a beautiful vessel, Mary of Guise showed her daughter—the large one, with the French standard. The ship would be full of surprises for her, and for all who were going with her.

The Queen Mother looked at the young face beside her. The deep-set Stuart eyes sparkled bravely through tears that brimmed, but did not overflow. Mary of Guise glanced at the galleys. Soon Mary Stuart would be taken down the long flight of steps from the castle and put in the charge of her escorts, Admiral Villegaignon and Sieur de Brézé, who were old friends of her mother. The Queen Mother dropped to her knees to embrace her daughter. These moments would have to last her many lonely days.

She looked again at those understanding eyes. Not once had the child begged to stay in Scotland with her mother. She had the courage her mother needed now. Mary of Guise knew that Mary Stuart would make a good queen.

A soft breeze caressed the tear-stained face of Mary Stuart's mother as she stood alone on the shore. She had steeled herself for this moment of parting, yet it was difficult to realize that those fading specks over the horizon were the ships carrying her daughter away.

She lingered but a few moments. Choking back a sob, Mary of Guise threw her head back, then turned to climb the castle steps. There was work to be done . . . for Mary Stuart, young Queen of Scots.

Chapter Two

A warm Breton sun beat down as Mary Stuart set her foot on the rocky shore of the little French port of Roscoff, six days later. The four Lady Marys with Nurse Sinclair and Lady Fleming followed, all as excited as their queen. The voyage was over at last!

The curious villagers, sailors and fisherfolk who had first seen the galleys approach were soon joined by peasants who hurried to the scene. These were no ordinary passengers. Wasn't that the King's own standard flying from one of the masts?

As the news was whispered about that the lovely child in the rose-colored cloak, the first of the little girls to step ashore, was betrothed to their Dauphin, François, knees were bent and heads bared in an impulsive salute.

Mary Stuart soon learned from Sieur de Brézé, in whose charge she would continue to remain, that the King, Henri II, and his Queen, Catherine de Médicis, were on an inspection tour of the border towns. They would welcome her shortly after her arrival at the Palace of Saint-Germain-en-Laye. There she would live with the royal children, the Dauphin François, his two sisters, Ysabel and Claude, and their baby brother, Louis. All France, he assured her, was glad she had come. The many welcomes she would receive on her journey to Saint-Germain-en-Laye would show how she was already beloved in her second homeland.

Bales and boxes were brought ashore. Nearby the cobblestone road rang with the sound of horses' hoofs. The bystanders saw the King's litters arrive for the royal party. Each litter was suspended between mounted horses, one before, the other behind. The metal-studded trappings of the gaily bedecked horses sparkled in the sunlight.

Spellbound, the five Marys watched as liveried attendants led lines of pack horses toward the piles of baggage. The children stood on tiptoe to glimpse the horseguard in the rear. It seemed to the little girls that everywhere they looked there were horses, men, and a bustle of activity. They could not make themselves heard above the din.

It was, however, the carved, painted, and gilded litters with their arched bows that most pleased Mary Stuart's eye. These conveyances were far more beautiful than those her mother had described. She loved the rich velvet canopies visible through the arches and the matching curtains at the sides of the open spaces and entrances. But above all else the royal arms, intricately carved on the end panels, fascinated her. Each had a huge H, for Henri, with crescents filling in the spaces. Mary Stuart spelled to herself the Latin letters of the King's motto, *"Donec totum impleat orbem"* (Until he shall fill the whole world).

Sieur de Brézé smiled as he watched the excited children. Each shouted enthusiastically, trying to make herself heard as she pointed out a new design or figure discovered in the conveyances that would carry her overland. The French nobleman could appreciate their delighted interest. In Scotland, no such art or mode of travel existed.

Sieur de Brézé enjoyed answering the many questions the observant child asked as they made their slow progress along the coast toward Morlaix. He must remember to mention them when next he wrote her mother. He smiled as the questions finally slowed down and the heavy-lidded eyes closed in sleep.

Despite the overnight stops, it would be a hard and try-ing journey for such a little girl. The King had sent word that the Queen of Scotland was to be welcomed with as much pomp and ceremony as though she had been a mem-ber of his own family. This, too, would tax the energy of his charge.

It was several days later that Mary Stuart's litter came to a halt before an old Dominican convent in the seacoast town of Morlaix. During their two-day stay here, the royal party attended a thanksgiving service in honor of Mary Stuart's safe arrival. The Scottish Queen gazed in awe at the most elaborate service she had ever attended. Was this really all because of her? Curiously she stared about her—sometimes she forgot about being a queen. She would try to remember. Her mother had said it was important to remember.

Later, as they journeyed by easy stages from Morlaix to-ward the south of Brittany and Nantes, the rocky coast they had been following changed to flourishing fields, gardens, orchards, and forests. Cattle and sheep grazed in the rich meadows. The countryside was like nothing Mary Stuart had seen before.

Peasants, villagers, burghers, nobles, town officials, and members of the clergy left their homes and tasks to greet her. Mary Stuart felt warm inside, as she gaily acknowl-edged their friendly welcome.

She liked the stone cottages of the peasants, with their thatched roofs. The fragrant pine forests refreshed her. She was delighted with the gay music and the lively songs she heard and the dances she saw.

At night as she lay quietly in her bed, Mary Stuart's thoughts often turned to her mother. But sleep always came quickly, stopping the little Queen's tears. And as one day followed another, the loneliness grew less. So many of the old, familiar faces were around her still, and new friends were rapidly becoming an important part of her life.

When they entered Nantes some days later, Sieur de Brézé and Nurse Sinclair found more of interest in Mary Stuart's expressive face than in the crowded and festive streets around them.

Nurse Sinclair was increasingly concerned at this succession of pomp and ceremony. Would Mary Stuart continue to be the same sweet person, the simple child, when this was over? She was so young! Nurse Sinclair would be glad when they could settle down at the French court, where Mary Stuart could resume her studies.

Far different thoughts occupied Sieur de Brézé. He watched eagerly for each sign of delight. Proudly he pointed out to his charge the many ways in which the inhabitants of Nantes celebrated her arrival. All this was for her!

When at last they sighted the Loire River on which they were to continue their journey by barge, Nurse Sinclair appeared anxious. She could see the strain and weariness, the dark circles beginning to line the child's eyes.

But the royal servant's concern soon drifted away as she sat with the five Marys, Lady Fleming, other Scottish attendants and Sieur de Brézé in Henri II's handsomely decorated and canopied barge watching the housetops of Nantes disappear. Although Nurse Sinclair thought there would be ceremonial welcomes along the way, she knew they would be few and far between. The boat trip would be quiet.

Day after day the royal barge glided slowly up the Loire. Each evening it was moored, so that its passengers could dine and spend the night on shore. The children could hardly believe that they were again traveling by water.

Their ship voyage from Scotland had been rough, but this one was as calm and as interesting as they could wish. The scene changed constantly as the boatmen on each side pushed their stout poles down to the river bed to coax their craft along.

There were towering châteaux, some with only a low stone wall, others half concealed among the trees ablaze with autumn colors. These imposing buildings, primarily fortress homes of the French kings, were in sharp contrast to the peasants' simple cottages. The children saw large vineyards with laborers picking clusters of grapes and laying them carefully in baskets. They passed meadows, some with cattle, others with sheep. Once they saw a red fox come out of a forest to drink at the edge of the river. They saw a startled heron take wing at the approach of the barge. Rounding a bend they passed harvesters loading sheaves of wheat and bundles of barley onto crude farm carts. Along the riverbanks fishermen doffed their caps, and women washing clothes paused, as the royal barge went by.

While her daughter traveled farther and farther away from her, Mary of Guise read with deep pleasure a letter from her own mother, Antoinette de Bourbon, Duchesse de Guise:

"I felt happier than I can say when I heard that our little Queen had arrived in as good health as we could wish for her. I grieve for the anxiety which I think you must have felt during her voyage, and before you had learned of her arrival here, and also for the sorrow you must have had when she set out. You have had so little happiness in this world, and are so much accustomed to have trouble and care, that I think you can hardly know what pleasure means.

"I will start this week, God willing, to meet her as quickly as I can, and to bring her to Saint-Germain, according to the King's instructions."

The lonely woman breathed a sigh of relief. It was a satisfaction to hear from her mother. She could rely on the Duchess to give her a true and accurate account. It was good, too, to know that her daughter would soon be with one of her own family, especially her grandmother. Mary of Guise was certain that her soldier father, Claude, Duc de Guise, would accompany the Duchess. Knowing the Duchess' piety and her scorn for frivolity, Mary of Guise had no doubt that her mother, as far as she was able, would see that the child's mind was filled with more important things than the gaieties of the French court.

Mary of Guise's thin lips smiled as she reread the letter. Even François I, it had been said, had stood in awe of her mother's severeness and austerity.

At the beginning of October, 1548, Mary Stuart finally reached Tours, where the long-awaited meeting with her grandparents took place. Nurse Sinclair had often heard the Queen Mother speak of Antoinette de Bourbon's unpretentious mode of living, and her dislike of display, and was pleased with the simplicity of the reception.

Mary Stuart was instinctively drawn to her grandparents. Her stately grandmother somewhat resembled her mother, although Mary Stuart did not think her grandmother was as pretty as her mother. She liked her grandfather's kindly eyes twinkling at her over his long, full-bearded face. And she loved them both even more because they belonged to her mother.

While the four Lady Marys were being presented to her

grandmother, Mary Stuart's eyes wandered about the small
gathering. Where were her uncles, the Duc d'Aumale and
the Cardinal de Lorraine? She looked again. Where was
her half-brother, François, Duc de Longueville? Perhaps he
was with the Dauphin.

Later that evening Antoinette de Bourbon settled herself comfortably at the writing desk in her room. Sieur de
Brézé, their host, had thoughtfully ordered fresh quills for
her. She looked up. Through the open door, Mary Stuart's
grandmother could see into the chambers which connected
with hers. Nurse Sinclair smoothed the coverlet over Mary
Stuart, then settled back comfortably into her chair by the
window. She strained in the fading light to see the needlework which she always had at hand. Softly she hummed a
Scottish lullaby.

The Duchess smiled contentedly. Mary Stuart was in
good hands. Nurse Sinclair would keep alive in Scotland's
Queen the memories of her own country. The child would
hear little enough of her native tongue at the French court,
so it was good that this woman would sing to her of Scotland.

Antoinette de Bourbon reached for a quill and smiled.
She was extremely pleased with her granddaughter. What
poise and alertness she had for one so young! Her mother
had trained her well. Scotland could well be proud of Mary
Stuart. Henri could be flattered. Was not this granddaughter not only Queen of Scotland but next heir to the throne of
England if Henry VIII's three children, Edward VI, Mary
and Elizabeth, died childless! France must not spoil this
child of destiny.

Dipping her quill into the inkpot, the Duchess bent over
a sheet of paper to write to her son, François, Duc d'Aumale:

"She is very pretty indeed, and as intelligent a child as you could see. She is brunette, with a clear complexion, and I think that when she develops she will be a beautiful girl, for her complexion is fine and clear, and her skin white. The lower part of the face is very well formed, the eyes are small and rather deep set, the face is rather long. She is graceful and self-assured. To sum up, we may well be pleased with her."

After a four-day rest at the family home of Sieur de Brézé, the royal party once more boarded the barge to leave Tours. Mary Stuart watched the lone figure of Sieur de Brézé on the riverbank growing smaller and smaller as the barge moved slowly away. The King had sent instructions for him to come south. Her grandparents would now bring her to court. She would miss her friend and traveling companion.

Antoinette de Bourbon made sure that the five little Marys did not miss any points of interest. Approaching Amboise, she spoke of the château high above the banks of the river. Here the Dauphin's grandfather, François I, had spent his youth with his mother. And for the first time Mary Stuart and her companions heard the name of Leonardo da Vinci, for it was close to Amboise that the great Italian master-artist had come to live at the invitation of François I. There the aging man painted wonderful pictures, sketched, and made plans for beautiful châteaux.

It was late afternoon when the royal party reached Blois, favorite resort of the French kings. Mary Stuart wondered at the many richly carved and gilded fireplaces of the château. In Scotland they were so much plainer and not nearly so large. Her grandmother told her that Blois had once been smaller and somewhat simpler, and that François I had enlarged and enriched it.

As the children climbed and made turn after turn on the huge spiral staircase, the great stair well echoed the sound of their hastening footsteps. Pausing, Mary Stuart gazed on the emblem of François. The flame-encircled salamander beneath the King's crown looked like a dragon.

Reaching the top, the children, Claude de Guise, and Nurse Sinclair stepped onto the balcony. Each child was lifted up so she could look over the high stone wall at the courtyard below. The little girls were astonished that the tall guards they had passed on entering now looked small.

At Orléans the royal litters awaited Mary Stuart and her party, to carry them overland for the rest of the journey. Once more the citizens had planned an elaborate welcome for her. As her gaze wandered over the colorful crowd, Mary Stuart's heart suddenly beat faster. That young boy eagerly approaching her—could he be her half-brother, François, the Duc de Longueville? Mary Stuart was oblivious to the welcome the citizens had planned. Her interest was in the slender boy whose smiling eyes greeted hers from under a plumed hat. Like his elders, he wore bouffant breeches, a short cape over an embroidered doublet, long hose, and square-toed slippers.

Within a few paces of Mary Stuart the lad stopped. Doffing his hat the thirteen-year-old Duke bowed low before his sister, the young Queen of Scots.

As the entourage moved northward through Orléans, the Duc de Longueville rode beside the swaying litter that carried Mary Stuart and her grandfather. So interested was the little Queen in her new-found brother, the first boy companion she had ever known, that she paid scant attention to Claude's story of Jeanne d'Arc, the young girl who had rescued Orléans from the English.

From Illiers, some days later, Antoinette de Bourbon wrote to Mary Stuart's uncle François, Duc d'Aumale:

"Our little Queen and all her train are as well as possible. I am bringing her by slow journeys straight to Saint-Germain, where I hope to arrive with her on Saturday next."

At Chartres, one of the oldest cities in France, the welcome peal of the great cathedral bells drowned out even the metallic ring of the horses' hoofs. Mary Stuart was surprised by the vastness of the interior of the cathedral. She looked at the colored light, deep reds and blues, filtering in through its stained-glass windows. She wondered if all the cathedrals in France were as big and beautiful as this.

Regretfully, Mary Stuart watched the young Duke and his attendants ride off in another direction as the royal party left Chartres to travel northward. She had liked her brother from the beginning. François was gentle and kind. His eyes and smile were like their mother's. In the little time they had had together she had told him all she could of their mother and Scotland. It would be lonely now that he had gone. Wistfully, the little Queen moved across the swaying litter to nestle in her grandfather's arms.

Chapter Three

Long before Mary Stuart's arrival, Sieur Jean d'Humières, governor of the royal children, had received explicit instructions from the King. Since the apartments at Saint-Germain-en-Laye that Henri had planned for his future daughter-in-law were not ready for the young Scottish Queen, the nearby house of Carrières was to be put in order for her. There the royal children and the little Mary Stuart would await his and Queen Catherine's arrival.

In a letter, the King had written to Sieur d'Humières:

"In answer to your question as to the rank which I wish my daughter the Queen of Scotland to occupy, I have to inform you that it is my desire that she should take precedence of my daughters. For not only is the marriage between my son and her fixed and settled, but she is a crowned Queen, and as such it is my wish that she should be honoured and served."

More details as to Mary Stuart's position came to the royal Governor from Diane de Poitiers, Duchesse de Valentinois, who wrote on the King's behalf that Henri's daughter, Madame Ysabel, and the Queen of Scotland should be lodged together:

"You will choose the best apartments for them and for their suite, for the King desires that from the beginning these two should become friends."

And Catherine de Médicis, alarmed over the reports of an epidemic in Paris, wrote at once to Sieur d'Humières insisting that no one from that vicinity be permitted to enter the house where the children were lodged. "I hope," she added, "that the number of my children may soon increase, and that they may have with them the little Queen of Scotland, and this gives me much pleasure."

Mary Stuart reached her journey's end two months after she landed in France. Flushed with excitement, she walked with her grandmother and Sieur d'Humières through the modestly furnished hall of her new home. Already she liked this French nobleman who had welcomed her to Carrières on behalf of the King and Queen.

At the end of the hall, doors were opened to let them pass, and then closed quickly behind them. Standing before Mary Stuart was the Dauphin, François, a pale, thin boy of four and a half. Beside him were the two little girls; the larger must be Princess Ysabel, Mary Stuart knew, and the smaller, Princess Claude. Keeping a watchful eye on all, the nurse held baby Prince Louis in her arms. Mary Stuart moved forward as the Dauphin and his sisters, Ysabel and Claude, smiled a shy greeting. Louis was the first baby Mary Stuart had been near. She laughed delightedly as he grasped her forefinger.

Still standing close to the baby Prince, Mary Stuart looked more closely at the other children. The Dauphin had not once stopped staring at her. The little boy knew instinctively that this girl would never laugh at him for his frailness and his lack of grace. He could trust her. Mary Stuart thought baby Louis nicer to look upon than this scrawny child, despite his silks and jewels. She looked away impatiently, but then remembered her mother's last words: she was to marry this boy one day; she must learn to love him now. With a sigh she looked back at him, and smiled warmly. Of course she would learn to love him—she must not let him know she felt sorry for him.

She approved of Princess Ysabel at once, and was glad they would share the same chambers. Mary Stuart was certain she was going to like her new home.

Henri was eager to have the little Queen become accustomed to her surroundings. The day after her arrival he sent word to Sieur d'Humières at Carrières that Mary Stuart's Scottish servants were to be replaced by French ones for the time being. He thought it wise to have Lady Fleming and the four Lady Marys moved to a different establishment. But Nurse Sinclair would remain with her charge, and Mary Stuart's grandmother would stay, too.

As Mary Stuart played in the garden on one of her first days at Carrières, she saw a rather tall man in a cassock coming toward her. A short beard framed his thin face, and when he drew closer, friendly eyes met hers. Mary Stuart smiled at her uncle, Charles, Cardinal de Lorraine.

With the passage of time, Antoinette de Bourbon and Sieur d'Humières were so pleased with the way the Dauphin and Mary Stuart had accepted each other that they could not refrain from writing to Henri at Moulins.

The King shared the good news with his wife, Catherine de Médicis, and then quickly wrote to Mary Stuart's uncle, François, Duc d'Aumale, saying:

"All who have come here after seeing her praise her as a wonder. This doubles the desire I have to see her, as I hope to do ere long."

While Henri's quill raced across the paper, Catherine de Médicis paced the floor of her chambers. It was ridiculous. She tried to brush away the thought but it kept creeping back. Already she was jealous of Henri's affection for this child neither one of them had seen! She knew from all re-

ports that Mary Stuart was a healthy, vivacious little girl.
Her son, François, was weak and sickly. Would this Scottish Queen shove her son into the background? Would
honor and praise come to him for what he was, only
through this daughter of Mary of Guise and James V of
Scotland? And would Mary Stuart, like all the court, be
won over by the King's friend, Diane de Poitiers, who had
the respect never given the Queen herself? Catherine knew
she feared this young Queen, yet she knew, too, that she
must never show her feelings.

Why, the Queen asked herself, did she so resent this
innocent child? She reached for a chart and began reading
her horoscope. Perhaps the stars would reveal the reason
for her uneasiness regarding the Scottish Queen. When the
court returned to Saint-Germain-en-Laye, she would consult Nostradamus, her official astrologer.

Meanwhile at Carrières, Mary Stuart was enjoying the
companionship of her future husband and his sisters. The
afternoon hours in the garden were well earned after a
morning of study, music, and dancing lessons. Here in the
garden Mary Stuart had her first riding instructions. Astride
a stick with a beautifully carved and bridled horse's head,
she learned to handle her reins properly. Happily she galloped on foot, or trotted after the Dauphin and Ysabel,
pretending she was following them in a hunt. She laughed
with pleasure at the spirited François. Despite his frailness
there was nothing he would not venture.

But the Scottish Queen most looked forward to the evenings, which she spent with her grandmother and Nurse
Sinclair. As they sat together in the candlelighted room
and Antoinette de Bourbon told of the time when Mary of
Guise had been a little girl, Mary Stuart thought how much
her grandmother's voice sounded like her own mother's.

She was grateful for her grandmother's thoughtfulness in allowing enough time for Nurse Sinclair to sing a Scottish ballad. These were Mary Stuart's most precious moments. As her faithful servant began to sing, the child Queen imagined she was again sitting beside her mother embroidering in a hearth-warmed room in a Scottish castle.

It seemed to Mary Stuart that she had just arrived at Carrières, when word came that Saint-Germain-en-Laye had been made ready for them. The King and Queen would join them any day. Mary Stuart did not know which excited her most. Was it the thought of seeing the King and Queen, or the idea of living at the spacious palace overlooking the Seine—the palace with its huge pleasure court, its beautiful formal gardens now autumn colored, and its nearby forest? Or was it that she and her four Lady Marys would be together again?

The day after reaching Saint-Germain-en-Laye the five Marys, the Dauphin and Ysabel were about to begin their dancing lesson when they heard the door open. There was a hushed silence as the King and Queen of France, accompanied by Diane de Poitiers, entered the room.

Mary Stuart was at once attracted to the rather tall, slender King. At twenty-nine he had dark hair, a short pointed beard, and a pale, narrow face. His brown eyes smiled at her. But she was not drawn to the short, plump Queen. Her dark eyes and prominent nose were forbidding. Nor were the double chin and full mouth attractive. However, the child Queen did like the tall, gracious Diane de Poitiers even though the older woman's mourning garments of black and white were less attractive than the Queen's elaborate dress. Diane's clear skin made Catherine's rouged face look dark and unhealthy by comparison.

The King stared delightedly at his future daughter-in-law. Catherine frowned as his thought, "the most perfect child I have ever seen," escaped his lips. But even in her chagrin, the Queen had to admit to herself, as Mary Stuart came toward them, that the little girl was lovely.

Compassion swept over Diane de Poitiers as she saw Catherine's face cloud at Henri's affectionate greeting to Scotland's young Queen. It was true that the Dauphin looked so small, so frail, compared to this charming and animated daughter of Mary of Guise and James V of Scotland. But Henri's love of children was one of his finest traits. His radiant face brought a smile to Diane de Poitiers. She enjoyed hearing him talk with the Dauphin, Ysabel, Mary Stuart, and her four Lady Marys.

For a moment Diane's eyes rested affectionately on Mary Stuart. She must keep her, too, among her friends. It was going to be interesting working with Scotland's young Queen!

Chapter Four

The weeks after Mary Stuart's arrival at Saint-Germain-en-Laye were crowded with exciting new experiences for Scotland's child Queen. Never in Scotland had she seen anything to equal them.

Not only were there many new friends to make much of her, but her handsome young uncle, the warrior Duc d'Aumale, of whom she had heard so much, would soon be coming to court. There he would stay until his father, Mary Stuart's grandfather Claude, Duc de Guise, arrived with the young Duke's bride-to-be, the seventeen-year-old Anne d'Este.

Even before the Duc d'Aumale came, preparations for his wedding were begun. Mary Stuart found them most exciting. For the girl Queen, as for the Princess Ysabel, there were slippers, elaborate cauls, and new clothes to be made of lovely silken cloth that shone with golden thread. In the bodices a court dressmaker painstakingly anchored row upon row of sparkling jewels. Although it was tiresome standing still so long, the little girls loved this part of the wedding preparations. They could hardly wait for the day to come when they could wear all this finery.

During one of these sessions Mary Stuart, clad in her new slippers and dress and wearing her hair in a jeweled caul, sat before a small table mirror enframed in gilt bronze supported by two standing figures. She smiled whimsically to herself, wondering if she looked as her mother had at this age. She wished her mother could see her now. She would like the beautiful dress with its full, full skirt and the lovely jewels. The child patted her hair. It was drawn back, French fashion. She pointed to a glittering slipper, so different from those of plain leather she had always worn in Scotland. Her mother had told her she would wear lovely clothes at the French court. She would ask Nurse Sinclair to write and tell her mother about them.

In the midst of all this, Mary Stuart's sixth birthday slipped by almost unnoticed. The usually thoughtful Nurse Sinclair was so busy that she quite forgot it. It was left for Sieur de Brézé, the friend who had escorted Mary Stuart to France and who was now once more a member of the French court, to present her with a little caged bird for the occasion, a yellow-green linnet whose songs became the delight of the nursery.

Sieur de Brézé continued to write full reports to Mary of Guise. A few days after Mary Stuart's birthday he wrote:

"As I have found means of letting you have news of the Queen your daughter, I did not wish to omit writing you this short letter in order to assure you that she is, thanks to our Lord, exceedingly well. The King has come to see her here at Saint-Germain, where she was with the Dauphin. I assure you, Madam, he gave her the best welcome possible, and continues to do so from day to day. He thinks himself most fortunate in that she arrived without accident or illness, and holds her to-day for no less than his own daughter. I have no doubt that if the Dauphin and she were of marriageable age or approaching it, the King would soon put the business in hand. Meanwhile he wishes them to be brought up together, and that their people should make one household. The reason for this is that they may early grow accustomed to each other's society. I assure you, Madam, that the King thinks her the prettiest and most graceful little princess he has ever seen. The same opinion is held by the Queen and all the Court.

"Madam, God granted me the happiness to place the Queen your daughter in the hands of Madame de Guise. I could not do such service as I could have wished to her and her company, and therefore I pray you very humbly, Madam, to excuse my faults if any of them should come to your knowledge, and to lay your commands upon me. In obeying them I will spend my life and my goods, as the most faithful and affectionate of all your very humble and very obedient servants."

Mary Stuart had no lack of guardians. Several days before the wedding, under the critical eye of her grandmother and Diane de Poitiers, the young Queen nodded graciously as measured steps became a part of her natural walk. Back and forth she went from one end of the room to the other. Diane de Poitiers and her grandmother often told her that she must have the carriage of a queen. Mary Stuart spoke determinedly to herself. She *would* have the carriage of a queen. Her mother was a queen. It was always lovely to see her mother walk with her head high, her shoulders back; Mary Stuart could almost hear the swish of her full skirts now. She wanted to be like her mother in every way. She *would* be!

The two Duchesses smiled happily as Mary Stuart turned her back and walked. She was an apt pupil.

Turning again toward her instructors, Mary Stuart started with surprise. A tall, rather slender nobleman had appeared beside her grandmother. As she drew closer, Mary Stuart could see his fair hair and thin beard better. The large blue eyes in his olive-hued oval face were like her grandfather Claude's. As he came forward and bowed, the little Queen knew at once that he was her famous warrior uncle, François, Duc d'Aumale.

The Duke smiled his approval as his royal niece resumed practicing her steps. How like her mother Mary Stuart was, even at this age! She was charming, quite pretty; her smile would win many hearts. It already had won his. He glanced toward his mother, and then at Diane de Poitiers. Mary Stuart could be in no better hands. His mother would do all within her power to keep the child's head from being turned. She would keep her as unspoiled as possible, and as much under her jurisdiction as she was able. She had never felt comfortable in the face of the intrigues and extravagance that seemed an inevitable part of court life. As for Diane, she had given the French court the best that it had today. She would see that the Scottish Queen, like herself, was familiar with only what was best in the court.

Mary Stuart felt like skipping, though she knew a queen should walk. She liked her uncle, François. Now she was eager to see his bride. She knew she was going to like Anne d'Este, too. Her cheerful mood vanished at the thought of Catherine de Médicis. If only she could like the Queen better than she did—she seemed so different, so strange. Although the Queen was kind, Mary Stuart felt there was no warmth behind that kindness.

At last the looked-for day arrived: the wedding of her uncle, François, and Anne d'Este. First came the solemn ceremony, and then the banquet and the great ball.

Mary Stuart felt as though she were living in a dream.

The handsomely embroidered doublets of the men, their bouffant breeches above long silken hose and jeweled square-toed slippers; each was lovelier than the last. She could hardly believe that the ladies' beautiful dresses, head-dresses and jewels were real. They looked like the figures in one of the tapestries at Saint-Germain-en-Laye. Her new aunt, Anne d'Este, was tall and beautiful—quite like her own mother, although younger. Mary Stuart liked her from the minute she first saw her. She hoped her uncle and his bride would stay with them at Court. But Diane de Poitiers—Mary Stuart's eyes always wandered back to her. She stood out amongst them all. No matter when she looked at Diane their eyes met. She knew Diane liked her. Once or twice she turned to glance at Queen Catherine. Mary Stuart smiled, but the Queen always seemed to look away. However, the King and her uncle, François, even her uncle, the Cardinal of Lorraine, were gay and happy. She liked the attention they paid her. Mary Stuart wished the Dauphin's mother would enjoy the ball as much as she did.

The musicians were tuning their instruments. The Dauphin stood before her—they, too, were going to take part in the dancing. At once the Scottish Queen was caught in the spirit of the gay melody. So absorbed was she in her steps and the music as she and the Dauphin performed, that she did not notice the other dancers had stopped to watch them.

As she glided gracefully with her partner, the King's face was aglow with pride. Diane de Poitiers and Mary Stuart's uncles exchanged delighted glances. Mary Stuart's grand-mother nodded her approval, though she could not help feeling that there must not be too much of this display for one so young and so attractive. Queen Catherine some-what bitterly let her thoughts be known, "This small Queen of Scots has only to smile in order to turn all French heads."

Then Mary Stuart sat with the royal children beside Diane de Poitiers and watched her elders dance. She blinked. The elaborately wrought candelabras on the four walls and the three huge chandeliers hanging from the ceiling of the long ballroom held lighted waxen tapers on every spike. The jeweled court costumes twinkled back at them—reflections of light. Mary Stuart had never seen a room glitter as did this. When she half closed her eyes it looked as though each candle were crowned with a cluster of stars. She turned to tell the other children of her thoughts, but the Dauphin was dozing and Ysabel already asleep. She moved closer to Diane de Poitiers but soon her eyes closed, her head drooped and she, too, slept.

Watching his niece, the Duc d'Aumale wished that the court painters were present. What a picture they made: Diane de Poitiers, Queen in all but name, and Mary Stuart, Queen by heritage!

If Mary Stuart had attracted favorable attention before at the French court, her appearance at her uncle's wedding completed her conquest of all hearts—all, that is, except the Queen of France, and the English ambassador. He had remained stern and cold, and Henri had noted his reaction. He described the incident in a letter to Mary of Guise:

"I should like you to know, Madam my good sister, that I had invited to the wedding of my cousin the Duc d'Aumale, your brother, all the Ambassadors of the various princes who are with me. He of England was not absent, and in his presence I took the opportunity of making my son the Dauphin dance with my daughter the Queen of Scotland. And as he was talk-

ing with the Emperor's Ambassador, my cousin the
Cardinal de Guise approached him, to whom I said
that it was pretty to see them. And my cousin replied
that it would be a charming marriage. The English
Ambassador merely answered that he found much
pleasure in watching them. Yet I am sure he found
hardly any, and he liked as little the caresses which he
saw me give them. Such, Madam my good sister, are
the tidings of our nursery, which I wished to tell you,
so that you may feel, over there, something of the pleasure which I enjoy constantly, and which increases
from day to day, when I see my daughter and yours
going on always better and better."

Mary Stuart's mother smiled as she finished reading.
Henri's letter was ample evidence of his wholehearted acceptance of her daughter. His dispatch showed that he
could give her all the protection she would need.

Chapter Five

Some weeks after her uncle, François' marriage to Anne d'Este, Mary Stuart's grandparents prepared to leave the French court for their home in Joinville, in the valley of the Marne. Antoinette de Bourbon, Duchesse de Guise, knew she could not stay at court any longer, much as she loved being with her granddaughter. The new year, 1549, was well under way, and there was much to be done at Joinville after such a long absence. Her husband, Claude, was far from well, and she needed more solitude for prayer.

The Duchesse de Guise felt no apprehension in leaving Mary Stuart, for she knew the reliable Sieur d'Humières would oversee the royal children, and she felt sure of the learned and brilliant Diane de Poitiers' love and interest for Mary Stuart, and of Henri's affection for the child. The Duchess' son, Charles, Cardinal de Lorraine, spent much time at court, and he would see that his royal niece had the proper religious and secular instruction. He was astute enough to handle difficulties if they arose. As for Queen Catherine, with all her superstitions and mystic charts, she was a devoted and conscientious mother and she would be most careful in her attitude toward the Scottish Queen. Mary Stuart's grandmother knew that she could not depend upon Lady Fleming, however. The attractive governess' head had been turned by the flattery and the glamor of the court, not to mention the King's attentions. But Nurse Sinclair and Diane de Poitiers would

send the Duchesse de Guise reliable reports of Mary
Stuart's progress.

At first Mary Stuart missed her grandparents, but the
months that followed were so full that there was no time
for loneliness. For now more than thirty of the high French
noblemen's children had become a part of the royal nursery,
and their small establishment had been increased by over
a hundred and fifty servants.

At first Mary Stuart found her expanded world bewilder-
ing, there were so many new names and faces all at once.
She was not quite sure what to expect from the older boys
and girls. Until now her half-brother, François, was the
only child she had known who was older than she. All her
playmates had been her own age or younger.

But, as she grew accustomed to her new circle of friends,
the young Queen welcomed the idea of their being a part
of the royal nursery while their parents were in attendance
at court. Certainly all her activities had been enlivened by
them. No longer did she, the Dauphin, Ysabel or the four
Lady Marys have to wonder who would take the roles or
act double parts in their masques. The same games they
had played over and over took on new life. It had been
monotonous to dance with the same partner continuously;
now the children's salon looked like a court ball, with so
many in tight bodices, long skirts, embroidered cauls,
doublets, bouffant breeches above long hose, dancing
happily to the lively tunes of their own musicians. The
boys and girls in their bright-colored clothes were just as
her mother had described them.

Now that there were so many more children in the royal
classroom, many tutors were needed. Mary Stuart was glad.
Even at this age she had a yearning for knowledge.

During these months the King often visited the royal

schoolroom. Sometimes Diane de Poitiers would accompany him, and at others she came alone. When he was at court Mary Stuart's uncle, the Cardinal de Lorraine, was a daily observer of his niece's progress. Queen Catherine, too, was a frequent visitor, but Mary Stuart noticed that she spent most of her time listening to the Dauphin struggle with his studies, and helping him when he groped for a word. Ysabel needed far less encouragement from her mother. Once in a while Queen Catherine would stop and listen to Mary Stuart recite in Latin. In these brief moments the child felt Queen Catherine's interest. Mary Stuart had been told of the Queen's great love for learning.

Occasionally, when lessons were over for the day, the King would visit with the Scottish Queen alone. She liked the way he talked. He treated her like a grownup as he told of the problems that she herself some day would have to face. It was not always easy to be a King or a Queen. There were wars to be fought in defense of right and of kingdom. Quite often a ruler's subjects were dissatisfied with the way they were governed. There were vassals who refused to acknowledge their ruler. And there was a constant battle to keep the Roman Catholic Church supreme.

As he finished, Henri watched the thoughtful face beside him. He was surprised at how freely he could talk to Mary Stuart. Despite her youth, he had the feeling that she understood his meaning completely.

The best that France could offer Mary Stuart was none too good for her. With satisfaction Henri thought of a few of the Latin, Greek and history scholars and literary geniuses already members of the royal circle. There was his own sister, Marguerite, as well as Pierre de Ronsard, Joachim du Bellay, and Jacques Amyot.

He was fortunate that his own father, François I, had accepted this new art, music and learning for his court. Now, on this background, he could build a far richer life for his own children and for Scotland's Queen. They could absorb all this beauty and splendor. His would be the most cultured and learned court of the day.

Yet he had not had much of the training one must have to rule. If only his father had talked with him as he now did with Mary Stuart, and as he would later with the Dauphin! He knew now that the arts and sciences were not enough of themselves to teach a king or queen to rule, just as winning a joust did not make one fit to lead an army.

But the King was not always so serious with Mary Stuart. Often he told her about the tournaments, the chase, and the chivalric games he loved. Sometimes he described a pageant, or a masque, or told her the story of a play.

Then there were times when the King and Diane de Poitiers took her and the Dauphin to the royal stables. Mary Stuart was always happy when Diane was with them. Her stories of the horses, the hounds, and the hunts fascinated the child. Diane de Poitiers always made everything seem as real as if her hearer were a part of it.

On one of their trips to the stables, Mary Stuart was surprised to find two horses saddled. She saw the King motion to the nearby attendants, and before she knew it both she and the Dauphin were mounted. The excited child did not see the King's pleased look, nor did she hear Diane de Poitiers' words of praise as she reached for the reins and handled them as the Dauphin had taught her when they rode their wooden play horses. But now a groom held both horses still. Mary Stuart could hardly wait for the day when she would really ride.

On one of these busy days Nurse Sinclair hurried Mary

Stuart into a cloak. Diane de Poitiers was going to take
her for her first ride in a coach! Many times Mary Stuart
had seen the carved and gilded horse-drawn conveyance.
It looked like the royal litter in which she had traveled
through France, but the coach was larger, and on wheels,
while the litter was suspended between mounted horses.

Some minutes later an elated Mary Stuart sat beside
Diane de Poitiers. The little Queen heard the door close,
and a whip crack; wheels creaked and they rumbled over
the road. She leaned back against the velvet-cushioned
seat. It was fun to feel the whole coach jog every time the
wheels rolled over a rut or stone.

Shortly after they started, Diane drew aside the curtain
at her window to let in a stream of sunlight. Mary Stuart's
small gloved hand pulled back her curtain. The child was
surprised to find that the trees and gardens seemed to pass
more quickly than when she rode in a litter. She turned
to look at Diane de Poitiers. Their eyes met. Mary Stuart
smiled; her mother had said she would like the King's best
friend, and she did.

From time to time the whole court moved from one
château to another. Mary Stuart wasn't quite sure why
they moved. But Henri had mentioned that it gave more
of his people a chance to have him among them. Diane
de Poitiers told her that it provided the opportunity necessary to make sure that each dwelling was thoroughly clean,
and she added that the burden of feeding the court was too
great a drain on the people of one community for them to
be able to keep it up for long. Mary Stuart had to agree
that it did take a great deal to feed the court. Nurse
Sinclair recently had told her that, just to feed the children
of the royal nursery and their hundred and fifty servants,
a single day's provision list included cuts of beef, chickens,

hares, pheasants, larks, partridges, calves' feet, seven geese, five pigs, two calves, sixteen sheep, thirty-six pounds of cutlets, seventy-two dozen small loaves of bread, and wine from five different merchants.

The studies and activities of the royal nursery continued whether the court lived in the country château at Villers-Cotterêts, the ever lively palace of the Tournelles in Paris, or luxurious Fontainebleau. But Mary Stuart most welcomed the move to Fontainebleau. Its beautiful gardens, lovely ponds, fountains, lakes, immense pleasure courts, and magnificent chambers and salons fascinated her.

Occasionally the Scottish Queen saw her half-brother, the Duc de Longueville. Although their meetings were always so short it barely seemed they had taken place, she learned to know and love him well in the times they were together.

From Joinville, Mary Stuart's grandmother kept in close touch with her son, the Cardinal de Lorraine, and with Diane de Poitiers and Nurse Sinclair. Her husband Claude was too ill to allow her to leave for a visit, or to have Mary Stuart stay with her. She must content herself for the time with letters about her granddaughter.

Full though her life was, Mary Stuart never forgot her mother. She was learning to write better now, and sent her own letters instead of messages through others.

In Scotland, Mary of Guise felt a pang of loneliness as she read a letter of Sieur de Brézé dated August 10, 1549:

"The health of the Queen your daughter, thanks to our Lord, is as good as you could wish it to be. We see her increasing every day in stature and intelligence. The King treats her with as much honor as if she were his own daughter, as I hope some day to see her. Meanwhile, until she is old enough, everything

possible is being done to make her and the Dauphin
get on well together. They are already as fond of each
other as if they were married."

Her daughter had been in France over a year! In a few.
months she would have her seventh birthday.

Mary of Guise felt the time had come when she must
plan to go to France. Not only did she long to see her
daughter again, but there were other pressing reasons why
she should go. Arran was Regent of Scotland but, in the
time that had passed since their Queen left for France, a
number of Scotland's nobles had come to believe that the
Queen Dowager should be Regent in his stead. With the
French King's support she probably could win this power,
but to do so she needed more French money and renewed
assurance that Mary Stuart's marriage alliance with the
Dauphin would take place. She knew her brothers and her
parents would add their voices to hers. It would be good
to see her family again; her mother and father were getting
on in years, so it would be best not to postpone the trip.
And there was her son, her first-born. Odd that fate should
have pushed her son into second place among her cares.

As December drew to a close the Queen Dowager's plans
had begun to take shape. She must not let another year
go by before making this trip. She would be with Mary
Stuart for her eighth birthday—sooner, if she could. After
all these years of grief and disappointment, 1550, she knew,
held promise of happiness.

Chapter Six

The weeks of 1550 had moved into April when Mary Stuart learned of the death of her grandfather. His son, François, Duc d'Aumale, now became Duc de Guise. Although Nurse Sinclair knew that Mary Stuart was too young to realize what the loss meant, she was relieved when word came several weeks later that Mary Stuart's mother was coming to France. Not only was the nurse happy over the prospect of the Queen Dowager's visit, but also she rejoiced that it was made possible by the success of the French and Scottish forces in preventing the subjugation of Mary Stuart's realm by the English. Then, too, the recent peace treaty between England and France had included Scotland. This French-Scottish alliance, Nurse Sinclair knew, made it easier for the Queen Mother to leave her daughter's kingdom of Scotland.

Mary Stuart was joyously excited at the thought of seeing her mother. She picked up her ankle-length skirt and ran toward the next chamber, where her four Lady Marys and Lady Fleming were sitting at their needlework. They must know about her mother's visit! Then she must tell Ysabel and the Dauphin—and Diane de Poitiers. Mary Stuart's pace slackened. She had forgotten that Diane had gone to Joinville to be with her grandmother. Of course the King and Queen would know—but Mary Stuart laughed at her own impatience. She had not stopped to ask Nurse Sinclair how soon her mother would be here. Would Mary of Guise come the same way she had? Would the King and

Queen meet her? Would they take Mary Stuart with them
if they did? Would her half-brother, the Duc de Longueville, come to live with them? She glanced hurriedly across
the hall where Ysabel was amusing Princess Claude. The
news would have to wait. Quickly the Scottish Queen re-
traced her steps.

As her flood of questions poured forth, Nurse Sinclair
could only answer the little girl vaguely. She promised her
listener that she would tell her as soon as she knew what
the plans were. Knowing the Queen Mother, however,
Janet Sinclair felt sure that she would write to Mary Stuart
herself.

It was not long after this that a happy Mary Stuart sat
at a writing table beside Nurse Sinclair. Before them lay
two letters from Mary of Guise. Nurse Sinclair laughed
good-naturedly as Mary Stuart recited their contents from
memory.

The young Queen finished. She reached for a sheet of
paper and dipped a quill into the inkpot. Then as Nurse
Sinclair watched with admiration, the seven-and-a-half-
year-old girl laboriously began to compose a letter in French
to her grandmother, Antoinette de Bourbon:

"From Saint-Germain-en-Laye
"3 June, 1550
"My Lady,—I have been very glad to be able to offer
you these present lines, for the purpose of telling you
the joyful tidings which I have received from the
Queen my mother, who has promised me, by her letters dated xxii of April, to come over very soon to see
you and me, and for us to see her, which will be to me
the greatest happiness that I could desire in this world;
and this rejoices me to such a degree as to make me

think I ought to do my duty to the utmost, in the mean time, and study to become very wise, in order to satisfy the good desire she has to see me all you and she wish me to be. I pray you, my Lady, to increase my joy, if it be agreeable to you, by coming hither soon, and to arm yourself with all the patience which you know is needed in the interim. Inform me, I beseech you, of all your pleasant news, and hold me always in your good graces, to which I beg most humbly to commend myself, . . ."

Mary Stuart paused. She must not forget her lovely aunt, Anne d'Este. She pondered a few moments then continued:

"and also to those of my aunt, whom I love the more for the good company she is to you. Praying God, my Lady, to give you health and long life, and all you most desire, your very humble and obedient Daughter,

Mary"

In the days that followed Mary Stuart found it extremely difficult to be a diligent scholar. Not only was there the excitement of her mother's coming, but also there was the new brother of the royal children, Prince Charles, whose birth on June twenty-seventh had caused great excitement both in their household and throughout France.

However, the little Queen's impatience was quieted by the great preparations that were being made to welcome her mother. There was a long speech to be memorized. One of her teachers had written it for her to deliver to her mother and all the distinguished nobles upon their arrival. Mary Stuart wished that she could speak her own thoughts, but Nurse Sinclair had told her that royal children had no choice in such matters.

One day a pleased Mary Stuart learned from the French monarch that England's Edward had guaranteed safe conduct for her mother, should she wish to travel by way of England. The French galleys were on their way to Scotland to bring her to France. The Queen Dowager should arrive at Dieppe toward the end of September. Her brothers, the Duc de Guise and the Cardinal de Lorraine, her young son, the Duc de Longueville, and other dignitaries of the French court would welcome her. Later, she would visit Joinville where Mary Stuart's grandmother was remaining in mourning for her husband, Claude de Guise.

The King could not greet his royal visitor at Dieppe, as he and Queen Catherine had been invited to the city of Rouen where the people were planning a celebration in their honor at about the same time Mary Stuart's mother would arrive. Since Mary Stuart would one day be Queen of France, Rouen had asked that it have the privilege of meeting the child Queen of Scotland, and celebrating her reunion with her French mother. Mary Stuart would have to go to Rouen with the King and Queen.

Mary Stuart's eyes smarted when she heard the news. She stared straight ahead. She knew if she looked to one side or the other the tears would spill over her brimming eyelids. Even though the King had pointed out it was an invitation which could not be refused graciously, she still wished she could be at Dieppe when the galleys bearing her mother came in sight.

Her lips tightened. The King, she remembered, had told her that there were times when it was hard to be a King or Queen. Did he know that for her this was one of those times?

At last the long-awaited day came. Mary Stuart was so happy and excited that Nurse Sinclair had to take her to task. With an effort the child composed herself and sat quietly in a corner of the litter she and Nurse Sinclair would share on the journey to Rouen. Mechanically, without thinking of the meaning of the words, she repeated once more the welcoming address she had memorized.

Then, impatiently, Mary Stuart watched. What a time it was taking to get all the pack horses loaded, and everyone ready for the journey! Finally she saw Queen Catherine and Diane de Poitiers emerge from the courtyard, each proceeding with her attendants to her coach. Last of all the King himself appeared, and mounted his spirited charger, and they were off.

To Mary Stuart it was as though she traveled half in a dream with villages and vales, houses and churches, forests and streams slipping by in an ever-changing panorama.

At long last they came to the city gates of Rouen. As they passed through the ancient portals, Mary Stuart was alert to everything around her. Eagerly she peered through the curtained opening of the litter. Once she caught sight of a man in kilts, surrounded by a noisy crowd of revelers. Her mother must be here now!

Mary Stuart called to the rider on the lead horse to hurry. Indulgently, he made a show of shouting at the people to make way for them. And then suddenly the Scottish Queen was being helped out of her litter, and guided up the steps of a pavilion. Through the waving banners she saw an archway. There stood her mother, arms outstretched to welcome her. Mary Stuart started toward her, then remembered her speech. She began reciting it, but the noise of the cheering throngs drowned out the childish voice. Uncertainly she looked at her mother, and her chin quivered. But before the tears could come, Mary of Guise had rushed forward to embrace her daughter.

There was a hushed silence. Then, as cheer after cheer went up for the Scottish Queen and her French mother, Mary of Guise released her child. When there was quiet, Mary Stuart delivered her unfinished address to her mother and her Scottish escort. With awe and pride the Queen Mother listened. She could hardly believe that this composed child, this lovely young girl, was the same Mary Stuart who had left her two years ago.

Her address over, Mary Stuart thought only of her mother. She could scarcely wait until they would be alone. There was so much to tell—so much to ask and hear. But Diane de Poitiers had warned her that she must not be disappointed if at first she could not have her mother to herself. Later, when the court had settled down again, they could be together more.

Mary Stuart and her mother, in the litter carrying them to the ducal palace of Rouen, traveled through the decorated streets of the ancient city. Mary of Guise's heart was lifted by the long cheers of the crowds.

A few days after they arrived at the ducal palace, Mary Stuart, her mother, the Duc de Longueville, the Cardinal de Lorraine, the Duc de Guise, Queen Catherine, the Dauphin, Princess Ysabel and Diane de Poitiers waited with other members of the court for the final procession in which the King would ride. The Queen Dowager could not keep her eyes off her vivacious daughter chatting happily with the Dauphin and her brother. It seemed to the pleased mother that Mary Stuart was now more a daughter of France than of Scotland.

Loud cheers rose from the waiting crowds. Mary of Guise turned her head. In the distance she could see the bright banners of the procession as it came into view. First came the religious orders. Behind them were the city officials, followed by merchants and tradesmen, all resplendent in their brightly colored raiment, gold buckles, and white feathers in their caps. There were floats, too, with nymphs and goddesses pulled by gaily bedecked horses. Soldiers in Turkish costume paraded past them; there were even some Brazilian natives in the procession.

Most spectacular were the six great elephants. Each carried a special display on its broad back: a villa, a church, a castle, a town, a ship, and one even had a tray with lighted lamps. After them, riding on a spirited steed and bearing his naked sword, was the Constable de Montmorency, France's Minister of State. And at last came the King, robed in white velvet and cloth of silver, a white plume waving from his hat as he rode his magnificent charger. Close behind their sovereign were the archers of the guard.

As the procession came to an end, Mary of Guise was breathless. She had almost forgotten how lavishly the French could celebrate. She looked at Mary Stuart, still sitting spellbound. This was all new to her. The Queen Mother wondered how much of it the child would remember.

That afternoon they left Rouen in a cushioned litter for their long journey toward Blois. Mary Stuart chattered about all she had seen—the gold buckles on caps, the banners, the colored garments, the gaily decked horses, and the amazing elephants. Mary Stuart's mother moved closer, lest she miss a single word.

Mary Stuart spoke of the things she had seen as they passed through the streets of Rouen. There was the huge, ornate clock. Had her mother noticed its blue and gilt face? Had she seen the graceful archways of the lovely cathedral? Scotland had no sculptured fountains, that she could remember, like those of Rouen. And there was the market square nearby, where Jeanne d'Arc had been burned at the stake. Had her mother heard the story of the Maid of Orléans?

Mary of Guise smiled to herself. Yes, this child of hers was exceptional—as all the letters she had received in Scotland had said.

Chapter Seven

Mary Stuart found the palatial château of Blois, which had housed her overnight when she first came to France, now the liveliest of all the French royal residences. Its chambers echoed with gaiety as Henri and his court settled down for a stay. Balls, pageants, masquerades, banquets, tournaments, and hunts followed one another in rapid succession. Nor were all these just for the grownups. Jugglers and acrobats were sent to delight the children of the royal nursery. Masques and concerts were prepared especially for their pleasure. But despite all these festivities, the children's studies continued.

Mary of Guise kept her daughter close to her. The days were slipping by, and the lengthy consultations for which she had come to France would soon begin. One never knew how quickly things of this nature could be settled. Besides, there was her visit to her mother to think about. She must make the best possible use of the time she could spend with her child.

At the time, Mary Stuart's health concerned her mother. At home she had not had the overrich food and quantities of wine that were served to the children of the French royal nursery. She noticed that the lone water carrier was not nearly so busy at meal time as the many wine servers. No wonder the Dauphin and his sisters were pale and so often ill. Mary Stuart and her four Lady Marys still retained their sturdy Scottish bloom, but Mary Stuart had told her mother of frequent stomach disorders, and Mary of Guise

had seen for herself the frightful mixtures Catherine
ordered administered to any ailing child at court. The
Queen Dowager was certain that the less medicine her
child consumed the healthier she would be. Yet she dared
not protest. Catherine was so sure of herself and of her
private soothsayers who advised the weird concoctions.

Mary Stuart's upbringing in the French court had its
good points. She rode daily on either Bravane or Madame
la Réale, the two horses which the King had given her.
The Dauphin often rode with her on one of his mounts,
Fontaine, Chastillon, or Enghien. Even Mary of Guise
shared Mary Stuart's excited anticipation of the day when
she would be allowed to go on a real hunt. Both the Queen
Dowager and her daughter listened enthralled as Diane
de Poitiers outlined to them the thrills of the chase.

When she was not riding, Mary Stuart loved to go to
Queen Catherine's private zoo. Two of the animals in it
were hers, for the King had given her twin bear cubs which
frolicked with each other all day long. Mary Stuart would
have liked to pet them, they looked so soft and round, but
she knew it was not safe. Her bears were much more fun
to watch than Queen Catherine's lions, which paced end-
lessly up and down their cage. As for the snakes which had
been sent from Africa for the royal children's amusement,
Mary Stuart always hurried by them.

The Scottish Queen liked to show her mother the lovely
colored bird she and the Princess Ysabel had tamed. It
flew about their chambers, and would sit upon their outstretched fingers until they called it back to its cage.

Amidst all this splendor and festivity, Mary Stuart
celebrated her eighth birthday. For both mother and
daughter the memory of the two birthdays when they had
been apart made this occasion more poignant.

Not until the beginning of the year 1551 was an anxious Mary of Guise able to gain the King's attention. He listened somewhat impatiently, for he had heard her plea too often. In the weeks just past she had waylaid everyone who had the King's ear to speak to him on her behalf. But if she had any hope that the matter would be settled quickly, that hope was soon dissolved.

Henri pointed out that Scotland had cost him large sums already, and that even a King could not be completely free with money. Was it not enough that he had given rich gifts and richer promises to everyone in her Scottish train? Now she had not only their support but his as well, to supplant Arran as Regent of Scotland. Whatever else there was to discuss he would go into later. Meanwhile the day was perfect for hunting.

But a promise of payment was not what Mary Stuart's mother had come for. It took more than a pledge to rule her daughter's realm! Bitterly she reflected on Henri's words as she watched one of the court balls a few days later. Was there ever a kingdom or court as wealthy as this? Why was it that Henri put her off with promises? Mary of Guise's concern over Henri's promise of payment was increasingly evident as the days slipped into late spring.

While the Queen Mother waited hopefully for a further opportunity to talk with the King, a plot to poison her daughter was discovered. Robert Stuart, a Scottish heretic who had been released from the French galleys and had become an archer in the King's guard, confessed to the crime and was executed. The court was shocked when the attempt was revealed; and, though relieved that the plot had been foiled, the child's mother was completely un-nerved by the episode and promptly took to her bed.

Scarcely had she recovered her composure when the court

was again rocked by an unprecedented happening. Lady Fleming, Mary Stuart's governess, was banished from the royal circle because of her lack of discretion, and was sent back to Scotland. Mary of Guise realized how much Mary Stuart would miss her. She hoped her daughter would like the new governess, Madame de Paroy, who was a devout Roman Catholic recommended by the Cardinal de Lorraine.

Toward the end of June, 1551, Mary Stuart and her mother moved with the court to Châteaubriant near Nantes, to receive with Henri the English envoy extraordinary. Mary Stuart's excitement at being at a new château and witnessing another royal ceremony helped to quiet her mother's uneasiness.

As the ceremony ended, Mary of Guise sat pale and silent while England's representative asked for the young Queen of Scots in marriage for his sovereign, the boy Edward VI. The Queen Dowager felt the steadying hand of her brother, now Duc de Guise, as she heard Henri's spokesman quickly decline England's offer.

The English envoy met the refusal with an immediate request for the hand of Henri's daughter, Elizabeth of Valois, the Princess Ysabel. To this proposal the King and his councilors finally agreed.

The Queen Dowager sat quietly as though in a dream. How she longed to be alone to give way to her joy and relief! She need never again worry that Edward would press to have her daughter for his queen. But she knew she must control her emotions. She must go through the hours of merriment ahead, affable and charming and gay. She smiled at the thought. Was that what the English dignitaries would think of Mary Stuart's mother?

As the days slipped into July, Mary of Guise finally

reached the conclusion that there was more to be lost than gained by staying much longer in France. She would leave early in the autumn. Henri, she now knew, would never fail her, and his promise of payment would become a reality. His eye was not on Mary Stuart alone, but on her kingdom as well. Meanwhile, the Queen Mother could not leave Scotland unattended much longer. She would spend a little time with her own mother at Joinville, and then she would go to Scotland.

During the summer months Mary Stuart and her mother remained with the French court, delighting in the continued round of festivities, as they moved to Tours, Orléans, and finally Fontainebleau. Then came the day early in September when Mary of Guise once again had to leave her child, in order to preserve Mary Stuart's realm. Mary Stuart and her mother sat in her favorite garden spot at Fontainebleau, watching a bird drink from a nearby pond. Mary Stuart could scarcely believe that her mother would be on her way toward Scotland in a short time.

A footstep on the path made Mary Stuart and her mother turn. Nurse Sinclair had come to tell them the royal litters were waiting. Mary of Guise rose. The time had gone so quickly! She looked at Mary Stuart plucking a flower. The child was lovely, tall, and graceful for her age. It was hard to leave her.

Nurse Sinclair looked away as Mary Stuart offered her mother the rose. Mary of Guise lifted the graceful outstretched hands to her lips. Mother and daughter clung to each other—then the mother tore herself away. Slipping into her cloak she took Mary Stuart's hand and hurried with her along the path.

Mary Stuart, watching her mother's litter move out of sight, felt Diane de Poitiers' comforting hand in hers. The

Scottish Queen responded with a brave smile, although her eyes were misty.

Mary of Guise had scarcely reached Joinville, where she would visit her mother Antoinette de Bourbon before sailing for Scotland, when she was suddenly called to Amiens. Here she found her sixteen-year-old son dangerously ill.

Several days later, while the Dauphin and his sisters hovered over their newest brother, three-day-old Edouard Alexandre, Mary Stuart buried her face in Diane de Poitiers' shoulder. She had just learned that early that morning her brother, François, Duc de Longueville, had died.

While grief-stricken Mary of Guise stayed on at Amiens for the last rites for her son, she received a comforting letter from Queen Catherine. The Queen Dowager discovered in the neglected French Queen a warmth and sympathy she had not expected. Mary of Guise reread the Queen's letter:

"Madam—I send this bearer to inquire some tidings of you; I cannot help thinking they must be bad, seeing the loss you have had, for which I feel more sorrow then I can express here. If I could lessen yours I should feel happy, for the greatest regret that I have is not having the power to offer you the aid and consolation that I desire. But when I recollect, Madam, that you have been so virtuous in all your adversity, I assure myself that you will not be less so now, and that you will find consolation in the Queen your daughter, in the time to come. You will receive the greatest satisfaction from her love and obedience, and she will recompense you for all your misfortunes."

The Queen Dowager's lips quivered: "In the time to come . . ."

In the third week of October, Mary of Guise took passage from Dieppe for Scotland. While the King's galleys bringing her mother to England's shores battled the stormy channel, Mary Stuart settled down to resume her life at the French court.

Chapter Eight

Before she left, the Queen Dowager had asked the Cardinal de Lorraine to be guardian and protector of his nearly nine-year-old niece, but even without this request the Cardinal would have continued to maintain close supervision over the young Queen. As it was, Mary Stuart had come to turn to him spontaneously seeking the fatherly guidance and support she had never had. While the Cardinal returned her love, there was another reason for his interest in her welfare and growth. She was the key to the continued and expanded power of the Guise family. Through her he could control the destinies of Scotland and, after her marriage, of France.

Despite his duties, the Cardinal was never far from Mary Stuart. When the royal family moved from one château to another, he frequently accompanied them.

While at Amboise toward the end of January, 1553, over a year after Mary of Guise's visit to France, the Cardinal discussed with Queen Catherine the upbringing of her children. The prelate was much impressed by the Queen's insistence that her daughters, Ysabel and Claude, be under her personal supervision until they married. Her older son, François, though only nine, now had his own separate household granted by the King.

To the Cardinal it seemed that these apparently contradictory ways of bringing up children could be merged successfully for his ten-year-old niece. Since her mother could not be with Mary Stuart, he was responsible for her;

and he knew that if Mary Stuart had her own establishment, separate from the court, it would be easier for him to maintain complete control. So many people were a part of her life now that it was difficult for him to be sure that no one was trying to undermine his influence over her. Even her tutors had to be selected, not only for their knowledge of their subjects, but also for their awareness of what would help both his niece's future and the house of Guise.

A few days later the Cardinal preceded the royal family to Saint-Germain-en-Laye. In a letter to Mary Stuart's mother he frankly stated his opinion:

"I would not, if I were you," he wrote, "permit that any one but yourself, or some one appointed especially by yourself to that charge, should command your daughter; and over such person I would be sure to keep a tight hand, as by that means you would always have more power. But, knowing her goodness, I can assure you that you will never receive from her anything but entire obedience.

"She is coming hither [to Saint-Germain] with the Princes and Princesses, and is bringing her train with all her wonted retinue. You must now consider what state you would like her to hold. In order to give you some guidance and suggestion, I have had a list drawn up of all the people who are with her, and of the increase that seems necessary, and of her probable yearly expenditure. I send you this list, and in each article of it I have noted with my hand what, in my opinion, ought to be done in this matter. Will you come to a decision on these points, and let me know your good pleasure, so that it may be followed, and your com-

mands obeyed. I think that in the list as it stands
there is nothing either superfluous or mean; (mean-
ness is the thing she hates most in this world). Her
spirit, I assure you, Madam, is already so high and
noble that she lets her annoyance be very plainly seen
because she is thus unworthily treated. She wants to
be out of tutelage and to exercise her independent
authority. If you think, Madam, that the scheme I
have drawn up is not on a scale sufficiently liberal for
her rank and quality, you can enlarge and increase it
according to your discretion. You must, at the same
time, give instructions with regard to the expenditure,
and see how the money is to be provided, so there
should be no arrears. You must not expect or hope for
any help from this side, because the King says that the
revenue of the realm is very small, and so he cannot
support her. And if in future the King grants a subsidy
for the fortifications in Scotland, he will have to make
corresponding deductions from her expenses here in
France.

"I must not omit to tell you that Madame de Paroy
is doing her duty as well as possible, and you may be sure
that God is well served according to the ancient way."

The Cardinal then suggested that, if his sister approved,
he would let Mary Stuart wear some of the family jewels
he was holding in safe keeping. He also suggested that the
Queen Dowager send some of her jewels to make her
daughter look lovely on special occasions.

While the Cardinal waited for instructions to establish
a household for Mary Stuart, his niece's education was not
neglected. He arranged that she should have the benefit of
instruction from the finest musicians, linguists, and men

renowned in the art, literature, and science circles of France.

Pierre de Ronsard, the greatest poet of France, taught the Scottish Queen the art of writing verse. She liked to hear him tell how, as a lad of thirteen, he had been a page to her mother. Mary Stuart was pleased when her rhetoric teacher, Antoine Fouquelin, told her that because she was his best pupil he was going to dedicate his book, *La Rhétorique Française*, to her.

Mary Stuart learned to speak and write French as if it were her native tongue, and made excellent progress in Spanish, Italian, Greek, and Latin. There were lessons in needlework, music, and dancing. Often Mary Stuart delighted her friends as she sang while accompanying herself on the lute. The Cardinal saw that his niece was properly taught the precepts of the Roman Catholic Church. She learned not only the formal words of the Bible, but also the meanings of the stories it contained.

With all the training Mary Stuart received, she developed a discriminating taste and sense of sureness about the individual things she liked. Already the ladies of the court had learned to watch her dress, and copy it for their daughters. Her room was cited by Queen Catherine as an example for the princesses, so tastefully had Mary Stuart chosen and arranged its furnishings.

The Scottish Queen often entertained herself by inventing devices for seals, using French and Latin mottoes. After revising them until they satisfied her, she had the gem-cutter carry out her motifs to use for seals for her own letters.

At the same time, the engravers were busy working on a coin which a Scottish coiner had designed showing Mary Stuart's head. This showed the young Queen's profile, with her hair drawn back tightly into a caul, and her shoulders bare except for a jeweled necklace.

Much as Mary Stuart loved and respected the Cardinal, she was never happier than when visiting with her other uncle, the Duc de Guise, his wife, and their small son. She enjoyed being in their lovely château at Meudon between Paris and Versailles. Her soldier-uncle could not have been more devoted if she had been his own daughter. He held her spellbound with exciting tales of his warlike deeds. In less serious moments he lavished surprise gifts on her. On one visit her uncle took her on her first hunt. In Mary Stuart the Duke recognized the fearlessness of the Guises. He told her:

> "My niece, there is one trait in which, above all others, I recognize my own blood in you—you are as brave as my bravest men-at-arms. If women went into battle now, as they did in ancient times, I think you would know how to die well."

Despite Mary Stuart's varied activities, there was always time to share with her good friend, Diane de Poitiers. The Scottish Queen looked forward to those moments. As Diane de Poitiers related incidents of court life, Mary Stuart often pictured herself in the scene. Later, the Scottish Queen put into practice suggestions that Diane de Poitiers had made during such conversations.

Although Diane de Poitiers was proud of the daughter of Mary of Guise for the acclaim given her and for her brilliant mind, it was the child's generosity, her solicitude for others, and her simple but charming manner that Diane de Poitiers appreciated most. She thought Mary Stuart deserved everything she was capable of giving her. She wrote Mary of Guise:

"As to what concerns the Queen, your daughter, I will exert myself to do her service more than to my own daughter, for she deserves it more."

As the days slipped by, the Cardinal, too, was delighted with his niece's progress. A report of Mary Stuart to her mother might hasten her long-awaited answer to his letter concerning a separate establishment for the young Queen. Enthusiastically he wrote to Mary of Guise:

"The Lady, your daughter, has so grown and is growing every day in stature, goodness, beauty, wisdom, and virtues that she is as perfect and accomplished in all things honest and virtuous as it is possible for her to be. There is no one like her to be found in this kingdom, either among noble ladies or others, whether of low degree or middle station. I must tell you, Madam, that the King has taken such a liking for her that he amuses himself in chatting with her for an hour at a time, and she is as well able to entertain him with good and sensible talk as if she were a woman of five-and-twenty."

Chapter Nine

"This day," Mary Stuart wrote to her mother, "I have entered into the estate you have been pleased to appoint for me, and in the evening my uncle, Monsieur le Cardinal, comes to sup with me. I hope, through your good ordering, everything will be well conducted." It was a proud eleven-year-old Queen of Scots who looked over the long banquet table.

For Mary Stuart's uncle, as well, this was a momentous occasion. But a few short weeks after the long-looked-for decision by Mary of Guise, the Cardinal had found a suitable château for Mary Stuart. Having her own household did not mean that she was cut off from the French court. The young Queen could have more freedom, more time for herself, if she chose, but, like the Dauphin, Mary Stuart would leave her home for frequent trips and visits with the royal family. Now she could have visits from them in return. The King had promised to come soon with the Dauphin, Ysabel, Claude and Charles. Their youngest brother, Edouard Alexandre, and their little sister, Marguerite, were still too young to be brought. Queen Catherine was more careful than ever with her children, since the death of two-and-a-half-year-old Prince Louis. Now she was keeping to herself until her eighth child, expected in a few months, was born.

The Cardinal looked appreciatively at his young hostess, regal in self-assurance. How fortunate that she was so willing to follow every suggestion he offered! Softly he talked to her of Scotland, and of how France had protected her kingdom. It was the first time Mary Stuart realized the role her marriage was to play in that alliance. The Cardinal explained that the Earl of Arran, Scotland's present Regent, was not fully trusted by him or by her mother. Scotland must have a regent loyal both to her Queen and to the Roman Catholic Church. The sudden death in July of 1553 of England's young King, Edward VI, meant not only that another suitor must be found for Princess Ysabel, but also that the alliance between France and England was weakened. Spanish ambassadors were already on their way to England to draw up a marriage treaty between Philip II of Spain and England's Queen, Mary Tudor. Those events made it more vital than ever that Scotland and France stand together.

The Cardinal spoke again of Arran, Scotland's weak ruler. The French King, Mary Stuart's uncle explained, had offered Arran the Duchy of Châtelherault, with a yearly pension of twelve thousand crowns and a promise of the command of the Scottish guard for his son if he would relinquish the regency in favor of Mary of Guise. Now, with Arran's acquiescence, they had only to wait until Mary Stuart would be twelve years old and could legally appoint her mother Regent in his stead.

Nearly four months later, in April of 1554, the courier brought the good news that Arran had resigned. Mary Stuart was jubilant. She wrote to tell her mother how happy she was that Scotland was now directly under the rule of Mary of Guise.

The young Queen looked up from the letter she had just written. Her mother was so busy, she reflected, that it was not fair to burden her now with a problem which her daughter had so far been unable to solve. It concerned her governess, Madame de Paroy. From the beginning she had found this woman difficult, unreasonable, and unfriendly. Nothing Mary Stuart did could please her and, as the young Queen had learned, when Madame de Paroy was dissatisfied she made her displeasure felt. Not only would she take Mary Stuart to task for real or imagined slights, but she would complain to Queen Catherine or to the Cardinal or to anyone else who would listen.

Mary Stuart put her quill down. There must be some way she could make the woman like her. She had felt only love and friendliness from everyone else at the French court. Even Queen Catherine showed no sign of her earlier resentment. But Mary Stuart wondered whether Madame de Paroy, whom her mother had appointed as her governess when Lady Fleming was banished, could have friendly feelings for anyone. Certainly she gave no indication of it.

The Scottish Queen rose from her writing table, and realized with a shock that Madame de Paroy had been reading over her shoulder. Without a word Mary Stuart picked up her letter and left the room. Madame de Paroy, she realized, would not be with her forever. She was getting old, and her health was failing.

Mary Stuart's natural talents and the added hours she was now spending on her lessons were rapidly making her the outstanding young lady scholar of the day. She far surpassed in accomplishments her four Lady Marys, who continued to study at her side.

The Scottish Queen was a stricter master than any of her teachers. Every morning before she left her chambers she wrote a letter in French to Princess Ysabel, and then translated it into Latin, in which she became almost as fluent as in French or English. Sometimes friendly notes were written round a quotation from one of the authors she had been reading in Greek or in Latin,—Plato, Xenophon, Cicero, Plutarch, or Erasmus. Sometimes they contained a story of a historic event that seemed important to her.

An occasional letter went to the Dauphin, but Mary Stuart realized that her future husband was more interested in tournaments, hunting and becoming a good soldier than in improving his mind.

As the weeks rolled into months, the Scottish Queen grew fast. Because of this, and because, too, she studied much, she indulged in the traditional rich foods. Inevitably, at times she showed signs of fatigue and indisposition. The Queen Dowager worried about the reports that reached her and asked the Cardinal the truth about her daughter's health.

After seeing Mary Stuart at the christening festivities for her cousin, the second son of her uncle, François, and Anne d'Este, the Cardinal answered his sister's inquiry.

"You may believe, Madam," he wrote, "that we had a good view there of the Queen your daughter, who is well, and indeed in the best health she ever had. I am astonished at what you have written to me about her being sickly. It can only have been said by malicious persons out of ill-nature; for I assure you she never was better, and that the physicians themselves declare that she is of a constitution likely to live as long, with God's help, as any of her kindred. It is true that she has had, now and then, obstruction of the heart, when she has forgotten herself and eaten a little too much; for she has such a keen appetite that, if she were to eat as much as she desires, her stomach would often be out of order; but I will have more care taken about her diet."

But Mary of Guise's mind was not really eased until she read these words from Mary Stuart herself:

"Madam—Although the Bishop of Galloway, the present bearer, is now going to you, and can render you a good account of the state of health in which he leaves me, I cannot omit writing you this little note, to tell you, Madam, that, God be thanked, I continue as well as I was when I last sent to you; and that I continue to employ myself in all things that I know to be agreeable to the King, my lord and father-in-law, and to you. Assuring you truly, Madam, that, since business will not allow me to see you now, the greatest pleasure I can take is to hear from you often, and to learn by your letters that you are in prosperity and health; and I hope frequently to be able to communicate such tidings of myself as may be to your contentment. Recommending myself very humbly to your good grace, and praying God, Madam, to give you, in health, a happy life and long, your very humble and very obedient daughter, Mary."

It was necessary at times for Mary Stuart to receive delegations from Scotland, and listen to their addresses and petitions. Although it pleased her to see her countrymen and to hear news of the Queen Dowager and her realm, Mary Stuart was careful in her replies. She had been warned by the Cardinal that she must offend no one, and must say nothing that would cause her mother embarrassment.

The Scottish Queen made sure that her mother always

knew what took place at these meetings. Shortly after one
visit she wrote the Queen Dowager:

"I must not fail to apprise you that the Abbot of
Kilwinning has brought me letters from my cousin, the
Duc de Châtelherault, and the other Lords also. These
I have shown to my uncle, Monsieur le Cardinal; and
by his advice I send you, in order that you may answer
them according as it shall seem good to you, fourteen
blank sheets with my signature: these I have merely
signed *Marie*; and fifteen signed *La bien votre Marie*;
and six signed *Votre bonne soeur Marie*."

Mary Stuart paused to look over the last six pages to
which she had affixed her signature. Messages could now
be written in her name to the kings and queens of other
countries.

Continuing with her letter she wrote:

"I pray you very humbly to believe that I will not
fail to obey you in whatever you may be pleased to en-
join, and to think that the chief desire I have in this
world is to be agreeable and very obedient to you, and
to render you all the services possible, as I am bound to
do. I entreat you never to speak, but to command me
as your very humble and obedient daughter and servant, for otherwise I should not think I could hold place
in your regard."

In the spring of 1555, twelve-year-old Mary Stuart was at
Fontainebleau with the royal family when Henri received
Queen Mary of England's ambassadors on their way to
Rome. The Scottish gentlemen in the English delegation
asked to see their Queen. Mary Stuart was glad to grant
their request. She was deeply affected by the love and rev-

erence they seemed to have for her. She would have to work hard to be worthy of the trust and honor of these, her countrymen. She questioned them closely about conditions in Scotland. And as they took leave she vowed to herself she would return to her own land before many years had passed.

It was a few months after this that the Cardinal stopped to visit with Mary Stuart in her establishment. He was amazed to see how tall and shapely his niece had grown. Yet though she seemed well and in fine spirits he thought her unusually pale. Perhaps she had been overstudying. When he spoke to her about it, Mary Stuart told him of meeting her countrymen and the self-imposed decision she had made afterward. How humble and undeserving their devotion had made her feel! She wanted to give them a queen they would be proud of—one who could match any queen or king of their day. She had been working hard on a Latin discourse, one she—

Mary Stuart left her sentence unfinished, and hurried to her writing table. She opened a portfolio containing a number of sheets of paper. Then she beckoned to her uncle.

For a moment the Cardinal stared amazed as he scanned a carefully hand-written Latin page. He lifted one, then another; finally he picked up the manuscript and carried it to his chair.

Long minutes passed without comment, as Mary Stuart sat opposite and watched his face. She wondered if he was pleased or displeased. The Cardinal smiled at his niece. Then he asked her to keep this Latin discourse a secret. When the Christmas festivities were over, he and Mary Stuart would join the King and Queen. Mary Stuart,

Queen of Scots, daughter of the house of Guise, would have a surprise for the royal circle.

In the great hall of the Louvre on New Year's day of 1556, thirteen-year-old Mary Stuart rose quietly from her chair beside Diane de Poitiers. A hush fell over the large chamber as she walked toward the center of the brilliantly candle-lit room. The swishing of her silk skirt rhythmically accompanied the scuffing of her slippered feet. Oblivious to the eyes watching her the Scottish Queen halted under a large chandelier. The warm candlelight brought a fresh glow to her oval face, and made the jewels in her handsome headdress twinkle. Sparkling eyes scanned a waiting audience, and then focused on the King and Queen. Mary Stuart spoke softly, but with assurance.

For a moment the Cardinal was startled as Mary Stuart's eyes met his. How like her mother she was! Mary of Guise had stood thus before an audience at Joinville. Instead of the present Latin oration in defense of learned ladies, Mary of Guise had recited a long speech from a play. Her hands had been lovely and white, like her daughter's. She had used them, then, as gracefully as Mary Stuart used hers, now. Mary Stuart's voice was as soft, her words as clear and effective, as her mother's had been; like her mother, she held her audience spellbound.

The Cardinal, back in the present, gazed at the faces around him. Henri's was radiant. Even Queen Catherine's sullen expression had brightened. Diane de Poitiers' eyes brimmed with joy. The Dauphin stared in awed admiration. The head of the aging Antoinette de Bourbon swayed from side to side; the Cardinal knew she was pleased, but perhaps was wondering about her granddaughter's future. The Cardinal looked attentively at the courtiers and ladies sitting close to the royal family. Every eye was on the Scottish Queen.

Silence enveloped the hall as Mary Stuart finished her discourse. Then overwhelming applause echoed through the chamber. Mary Stuart tingled with excitement at the ovation. She waited a moment to conceal her emotion. Then she acknowledged her appreciation with a quick smile and a wave of her hand.

The King went to meet her. Diane de Poitiers watched this girl of promise. She prayed that Mary Stuart would always have the graciousness, the wisdom, love, and freedom that surrounded her during these blossoming years of her life.

Chapter Ten

Before her table mirror Mary Stuart raised her hand to put a strand of hair in place, and caught a glimpse of Madame de Paroy in the glass. She shrugged as she watched the woman run her hand over the dress she was about to put away. It was as though she thought it hers already.

The Scottish Queen gritted her teeth. Madame de Paroy was becoming unbearable. The young girl dreaded every minute with her now. She had been able to control herself thus far, but she realized that she could not stand her governess much longer without saying something to her mother. She thought of speaking of it to Diane de Poitiers, but when she was with her, Mary Stuart had no desire to discuss Madame de Paroy. Perhaps she would speak of it next time. She felt certain that Madame de Paroy had complained to Queen Catherine during their last visit to the court. She had seen the woman come from the Queen's chambers and slip by quickly, as her mistress with the Princesses Ysabel and Claude and her four Lady Marys was returning from the garden. That evening the Dauphin's mother had mentioned something about being more considerate of her governess.

Later, however, when Madame de Paroy had talked with her grandmother and the Cardinal in front of Mary Stuart, the woman had nothing but praise for the young Queen of Scots. Mary Stuart could have cried out then, and told them that all the governess' words were meaningless flattery. How she loved this young Queen and wished she were

34442

capable of doing more for her! The long hours she spent in prayer to be guided to do what was best for her! Surely if Madame de Paroy made such deceptive statements to her grandmother and her uncle, she must be just as deceitful in letters to her mother.

Mary Stuart sighed. If she could get her uncle, the Cardinal, to listen to her! But whenever she mentioned Madame de Paroy, the Cardinal would interrupt, praising the woman. Her uncle, François, Duc de Guise, would more than likely have interceded for her, but he was away on a mission for France. To complain to Janet Sinclair and her husband, John Kemp, who was now Mary Stuart's *valet de chambre*, would be useless. All these faithful servants and friends could do was to give her comfort and understanding.

Mary Stuart clenched her hands until they were numb. She would wait a little longer, but she was determined to write her mother if Madame de Paroy did not alter her ways.

Meanwhile, she would devote herself more vigorously to her studies. There were not many years left to prepare herself for the responsibilites of being a queen. Already materials had been bought and dressmakers were busy readying the new, more grown-up wardrobe which she would be expected to wear after her fourteenth birthday. Her Lady Marys would be having new clothes, too; Mary Stuart smiled—they were all growing up. The Scottish Queen had received permission from her mother to dispose of her richly jeweled wardrobe of young girl costumes as she wished, when the time came. She had decided that some of her garments would go to several of the churches in which she had worshiped, where they could be made into curtains for the chancels or altar coverings. A few things she would give to her close friends. There would be something for

Janet Sinclair, too—treasured as much for sentiment, Mary Stuart knew, as for value. Madame de Paroy, she supposed, would try to interfere here as she did with so much else.

But her problems with Madame de Paroy paled into insignificance when Mary Stuart learned from her uncle, the Cardinal, that he and his brother were both deeply concerned lest Henri yield to the pressure of factions both within and outside his kingdom which were working to prevent her marriage to the Dauphin. The Guises would not rest easily until the marriage actually had taken place. If anything should happen to Henri, they felt, France's promise would not be kept.

Even at this hour the King's Minister of State, the Constable de Montmorency, and his supporters were suggesting to the King that Mary Stuart's marriage to the Dauphin would involve great loss of blood and treasure to France— which could ill be spared—to keep the turbulent nobles of Scotland in obedience to their sovereign, unless she and her husband were residing among them, and that Scotland was too remote and poor to become a valuable province of France; whereas if Mary were married to a French prince or great noble, who would assist in keeping up the ancient alliance between the two realms, it would be better for all parties.

Mary Stuart frowned. There seemed no end to her responsibilities and worries. Yet she did not think it fair to ask others to share her problems. François, who was as devoted to her as she was to him, gave no indication in the frequent times they now spent together that he knew anything of the intrigues that threatened their marriage.

The French King, however, considered no one other than Mary Stuart for his son's wife and future Queen of France. By April 8, 1556, the Cardinal wrote Mary Stuart's mother that it was the King's intention that the wedding take place during the coming year. The Cardinal added, "I can sincerely assure you, that no one can be more charming, or more excellent, than the Queen your daughter; and she is also very religious. She governs both the King and Queen."

Although anxious to see her daughter, Mary of Guise realized that this was not the time to leave Scotland. There was far too much discord among the Scottish nobles. In England, with Mary Tudor on the throne, Roman Catholicism had once more become the established religion. English Protestant refugees fleeing to Scotland posed an added problem for her.

In France the coming of summer, usually so welcome, brought a series of misfortunes to the members of the court. It was hot with an oppressiveness that seemed to drain one's strength. As the days wore on the King became more and more concerned over Queen Catherine. She was not well, and another baby was expected soon. Henri felt no joy toward the end of July when he dispatched a courier to tell Mary Stuart that Queen Catherine had given birth to twin girls, Princesses Victoire and Jeanne. Jeanne had not lived, and Victoire was frail and sickly.

In August Mary Stuart and her ladies moved to Fontainebleau to visit the convalescing Queen Catherine, the princesses, and their new sister, Victoire. The air at the château, usually so invigorating, was stifling. Even the woods seemed close as Mary Stuart wandered through them. She had never known such heat.

Scarcely had the Scottish Queen and her four Lady Marys settled down when Mary Stuart was stricken with a fever. The court physicians and attendants stayed close by. The Cardinal and the King, away at the time, were notified.

The royal circle anxiously kept watch outside her bedchamber.

Hastening to Fontainebleau as soon as he received the message, the Cardinal found the illness of his niece graver than he had feared. Immediately he wrote the Queen Dowager giving all the details.

Mary Stuart seemed to be the victim of a malady which had been all too widespread that summer. The Dauphin was ill, too, and the tiny Princess Victoire died. The little son of Mary Stuart's uncle, François, and Anne d'Este had to be kept in bed.

When the Cardinal wrote Mary of Guise again, two months later, Mary Stuart had been free of the fever for ten days. His main concern was to build up her strength.

Mary Stuart, still in bed, felt an overwhelming gratitude for those whose tender care had shown their devotion. Nurse Sinclair had been by her bedside every time she opened her eyes. The Cardinal had been there almost constantly. Now he had taken her with him to the Maison de Guise, the family home in Paris. The Dauphin was resting at the Palace of the Tournelles after another attack of a high fever, she had been told, and when the King and Queen came to visit her each day they brought loving messages from their son. How considerate all these people were! Mary Stuart was impatient to get well so she could do something to show them how highly she valued their loving care.

Not until her fourteenth birthday, in December, did Mary Stuart begin to be her healthy energetic self. Standing in her room, dressed for the first time in one of her grown-up garments, she looked pensively over the wardrobe that she was no longer to use. The time had arrived to dispose of her young girl costumes as she wished. She hoped that the recipients would be as pleased as she would be in giving them.

Unmindful of Madame de Paroy's harsh glances, the Scottish Queen happily selected three of the most costly gowns for use in the churches. Then she chose simpler ones for her personal attendants. As she started to pick out others for further distribution, Madame de Paroy exclaimed, angrily, "I see you are afraid of my enriching myself in your service; it is plain you intend to keep *me* poor!" Seizing the opportunity to play upon the young Queen's sensitive nature, the malicious woman declared that she was certain that the consciences of those who received the garments would be greatly burdened. Then, as harshly as she could, she told the astounded Queen that she was going to write her mother at once and tell her how her daughter had deprived her of the control of her wardrobe, and how little discretion Mary Stuart had used in disposing of her valuable possessions.

Mary Stuart was too stunned by the scene to answer. Trembling, she watched the door close behind her governess. What a disagreeable woman she was! Mary Stuart was glad she had not demeaned herself by replying.

After the young Queen had had enough time to compose herself and think over the whole episode, she wrote her mother:

"I know very well that she wrote a letter to you, telling you that I prevented her from having any further authority over my wardrobe, and would not permit her to take charge any more of that department. Madam, I very humbly beseech you to believe that there is nothing in all this; for, in the first place, I never prevented her from having power over my wardrobe, because I well knew I ought not to do it; but I merely told John, my *valet-de-chambre*, that when she wished to take

anything away he should apprise me, for, otherwise, if
I wanted to give it away I might find it gone. As to
what she has written to you of my having always had
power to do what I pleased with my things, I can assure you I have never been allowed by her the credit
of giving away so much as a pin, and thus I have ac-
quired the reputation of being niggardly, insomuch
that several persons have actually told me that I did
not resemble you in that. I am surprised how she
could dare to write to you anything so opposed to
truth. I will send you an inventory of all the clothes
I have had since I came to France, that you may see
the control she has exercised; and I beseech you very
humbly, Madam, to give credit to all the explanations
on that list."

The Scottish Queen reread what she had written. She
disliked composing such a letter, especially to her mother.
This was the first time she had really complained to her
mother or anyone else. Madame de Paroy had given her no
choice. Had she written more fully before, she might have
spared herself this unhappy predicament. Surely if her
mother had understood how things were she would have
given orders that Madame de Paroy be replaced.

Mary Stuart concluded her writing with an affectionate
allusion to her uncle and aunt, the Duc and Duchesse de
Guise:

". . . who take as much care of me and my concerns
as if I were their own child. As for my uncle, Monsieur
le Cardinal, I need not speak of him, since what he does
is so well known to you; I pray you to write and thank
them for their kindness to me, and beg them to continue
the same, for their care of me is incredible. I can say
no less for Madame de Valentinois [Diana de Poitiers]."

The year 1557 had just begun when the Cardinal came to visit his niece. They talked at length about Madame de Paroy. At first Mary Stuart was reluctant to say anything—after all, it had been at the Cardinal's suggestion that her mother had engaged the woman. She could hardly expect him to urge her mother now to dismiss her. But the Scottish Queen could not hide her thinness and the obvious strain she was under, and so, bit by bit, he coaxed the story from her.

The Cardinal was shocked. He had not realized how bad the situation was. Madame de Paroy was getting on in years, but that was no excuse. Her smooth tongue and piety had fooled them all. He must get Mary Stuart away from this atmosphere if only for a little while. He would take her to his château at Villers-Cotterêts. He would have to phrase his letter to the Queen Dowager carefully. After all, he had recommended Madame de Paroy.

Although he had been at Villers-Cotterêts for some weeks with his niece, it was not until April that the Cardinal wrote his sister. He began by telling the Queen Dowager that Madame de Paroy was apparently suffering from dropsy, and because frequent long absences from her duties had kept her away from her post for several months, he felt that a change was desirable.

"It displeases me," he continued, "to see the Queen your daughter, at her time of life, without having a suitable person with her; although she is so discreet and virtuous that she could not conduct herself better, or more prudently, if she had a dozen *governantes*."

The Cardinal reread his letter, then impulsively added a postscript:

"As to Madame de Paroy, she is a good woman; but you and all your race will have cause for lasting regret, if her remaining costs you the life of the Queen, your daughter, who has, with extreme patience, endured much, that she and I have thought could not but be known. But time at last unveils many things which it is no longer possible to bear."

He ended by informing the Queen Dowager of the King and Queen's desire to have the Comtesse de Brêne, a woman of high rank, take the place of Madame de Paroy.

The Cardinal could hardly believe the words he read when the Queen Dowager replied that she would not agree to Madame de Paroy's dismissal. How could she have failed to understand the danger?

Urged by the Cardinal and her grandmother, Mary Stuart wrote her mother:

"They are convinced," she explained to Mary of Guise, "that you would not wish to have anything in my household which gives occasion for people to make unpleasant remarks. Now, Madam, truth to tell, I have less occasion to feel satisfied with Madame de Paroy than with any woman in the world; for, as the Cardinal my uncle will bear witness, she has done what she could to deprive me of the affection of my lady grandmother, and also of that of the Queen of France. But I never should have dared to explain myself so plainly to you, unless my uncle, who has understood all that has passed on both sides, had not told me to speak boldly, and tell you that I think she has nearly been the cause of my death, from the fear I have had of losing your regard, and the vexation I have suffered from hearing so much mischief was made by her false reports, which were most injurious to me. Moreover, it is a shame that, for the last five months, she has not slept two nights in my chamber. Wherefore, Madam,

I humbly entreat you to signify (which I know will be very agreeable to the Queen of France) that I prefer having one of her choosing—namely, Madame de Brêne, with whom I should esteem myself very happy for the time to come."

As the summer of 1557 progressed, Mary Stuart's difficulties with Madame de Paroy were put aside. France's peace was broken by war with Spain. The disastrous defeat of St. Quentin in August and the capture of the Constable de Montmorency gave the Guises an added reason to renew their pressure on the King, to gain his consent to their niece's early wedding.

Henri, concerned over the French reverses at St. Quentin, could see that tightening the bonds between France and Scotland would be vital in the event England decided to strike. Accordingly, in October Henri addressed a letter to the Scottish Estates requesting that they send commissioners to France to arrange their Queen's marriage and to cement further the ancient alliance between the two countries.

While France awaited the arrival of the Scottish representatives, the Duc de Guise, early in 1558, seized and captured Calais, the only remaining English possession in France. It was as great a victory for the French as it was a humiliation for the English.

For Mary Stuart there had been another victory as important to her as the military success of France's armies. At long last Madame de Paroy had been vanquished and had made strategic withdrawal. Not that she had wanted to go; far from it. Mary Stuart did not ask what had taken place. It was enough for her to know that at the Cardinal's orders Madame de Paroy's effects had been packed for her and dispatched to Paris. Madame de Paroy had been personally escorted by the Cardinal from Mary Stuart's château to the litter which was waiting to take her away.

In the young Queen's household, the whole atmosphere changed when the Comtesse de Brêne replaced Madame de Paroy; Mary Stuart felt stronger, free from strain. Her grandmother remarked how well she looked.

Mary of Guise's representatives would soon arrive in France. There would be firsthand word of her mother. It was a pity the Queen Dowager could not be with them, but Scotland needed her at home.

Lord James Stuart, Prior of St. Andrews, would be among the commissioners. He was the Scottish Queen's half-brother, son of her father, James V of Scotland. Though he was considerably older than she or the Duc de Longueville, she hoped he would be as warm and friendly as her other brother had been.

Mary Stuart was excited because she and François were soon to be together, forever she hoped. Ever since the King had sent his letter to the Estates, every available court dressmaker, tailor, milliner, jeweler, shoemaker and goldsmith had been busy preparing the trousseaux for both the Dauphin and herself. She had learned to love François as her mother had said she should. Now they could ride, hunt, attend tournaments and masques, and have their own court and activities to suit themselves. But even though François would rather play, there must be time for her to learn all she could. Was not this marriage, as her uncles had repeatedly told her, to bring her country and her mother's together as one?

When the Scottish commissioners arrived in March, Mary Stuart was at Fontainebleau with the royal family. Her grandmother and her uncle were with her to welcome these important dignitaries. The Cardinal watched the bearded faces. He smiled to himself as he saw their startled but pleased expressions when they were presented to their tall, attractive young Queen. Her rich brown hair was drawn back neatly in a jeweled caul, and her dark Stuart eyes smiled at them from a flushed, oval face.

Mary Stuart felt a warm glow as she viewed her subjects. They were sturdy, and even though they wore none of the finery and had none of the gallant manners of the French, they were a fine, healthy-looking lot, and she was proud of them.

Since the commissioners had come to arrange the marriage of Mary Stuart and the Dauphin, the Scottish Queen immediately empowered them to act, with her grandmother, for her and settle the terms of the contract.

In April the marriage terms were agreed upon, and Mary Stuart promised to keep the laws and liberties of Scotland as they had been kept before by Scotland's illustrious kings.

Four days later, both the King and the Dauphin agreed to respect the liberties of Scotland, but with a provision that, should the Queen of Scots die without issue, their nearest heir should be her successor to the Scottish crown.

That same day, April 19, 1558, the fifteen-year-old Queen of Scots and the fourteen-year-old Dauphin of France were solemnly betrothed in the great hall of the Louvre. In the presence of the court, churchmen, dignitaries, and Mary Stuart's nine commissioners, the marriage articles were ratified and signed. The Cardinal de Lorraine officiated at the ancient ceremony of the joining of hands. The Dauphin then declared that of his own free will and with the fullest consent of the King and Queen his father and mother, being duly authorized by them to take the Queen of Scotland for his wife and consort, he promised to espouse her on the following Sunday, April 24, in the face of the holy Church.

In like manner the Scottish Queen also affirmed that of her own free will and consent, and by the advice of her lady grandmother, the Dowager Duchess of Guise, and the deputies of the three Estates of Scotland, she took the Dauphin François for her lord and husband, and promised to espouse him on the above-named day, in the face of the holy Church.

The great ball which followed, that evening, ended the festivities. All eyes turned to watch the lovely young Queen of Scots leading the first dance with Henri II, King of France.

Chapter Eleven

Five days later, on Sunday April 24, 1558, as the rosy dawn pierced the sky over Paris, every street, lane, and available spot adjoining the Cathedral of Notre-Dame was thronged with joyous spectators. This was the wedding day of their Dauphin François and his bride, the Queen of Scots. The first time in over two hundred years that a Dauphin of France had been married in Paris, this was a gala occasion for all France.

The large area in front of the west façade of the cathedral was dense with people. At the King's command, Charles le Conte, the court architect, had here built a raised arched platform and gallery. The marriage procession would pass there, and on it the ceremony could be celebrated in full view of all. The structure extended from the Bishop's palace to the church door. Its trellis of carved leaves and branches resembled a cathedral cloister. Before the great doors of Notre-Dame was a platform with a raised canopy of blue Cyprus silk, richly embroidered with the golden fleurs-de-lis of France and the royal arms of Scotland with their tressured lion rampant. A matching blue velvet carpet powdered with fleur-de-lis covered the floor. Assembled within were nobility of France and visiting dignitaries. The people waited impatiently for the royal procession.

In the Archbishop's palace, where the royal family had spent the night, Mary Stuart stood by her chamber window. She blinked back the tears that seemed to want to crowd out her happiness. There was only one thing needed to complete this important event. Her mother had been unable to leave Scotland. As she stood wrapped in longing thoughts of her mother, a fanfare of trumpets, softer viols and zithers, shrill fifes and the brisk rattle of drums shattered the quiet. At the same time Mary Stuart heard someone enter the room. Turning, she saw her four Lady Marys, each attired in brocaded silk. They had come to spend a few moments with their queen before she was caught up in the excitement of the wedding ceremony, and the elaborate celebrations and festivities to follow.

With a smile of tenderness Mary Stuart welcomed her friends, secure in the knowledge that these playmates of her childhood would be her intimate companions in her new life.

On the stroke of eleven, as trumpets announced to the gathered multitudes the start of the royal procession, the doors of the cathedral opened. Before them appeared Eustache du Bellay, Archbishop of Paris, with his cross-bearer and attendants. No sooner had the prelate emerged than the eyes of the throng were drawn to the palace door. The Grand Master of the Day, popular François, Duc de Guise, led the procession across the temporary gallery. Behind him came a brilliant array of musicians in red and yellow playing melodiously upon their instruments. Following were a hundred gentlemen of the King's household and many royal princes of the kingdom, all richly adorned.

A murmur ran through the crowd as the dignitaries of the Church began to appear. Eighteen bishops and mitred abbots bearing crosses preceded the Archbishop, the Cardinals de Bourbon, Guise, and Lorraine, and the Cardinal Legate of Rome, in their elaborate vestments.

There was a break in the procession—and then, from the palace doorway, came the serious-faced fourteen-year-old

Dauphin in heavily jeweled robes, escorted by the King of
Navarre. Behind them were the Dauphin's two brothers,
Princes Charles and Edouard Alexandre.

The trumpets, followed by lighter music, brought the
crowd's attention again to the palace doorway. Standing
between the King and the Duc de Lorraine was the Scottish
Queen. She was radiant in silver bridal gown sparkling with
precious stones. Upon her head rested a golden crown
studded with diamonds, pearls, sapphires, and emeralds.
The sunlight seemed to focus on her and was reflected from
the priceless jewel suspended by a chain of precious stones
which she wore around her neck, a gift from her great-
grandfather, Henry VII of England, to her father's mother,
Margaret Tudor. Over her shoulders hung a purple man-
tle richly embroidered with gold. Its six-foot train was
supported by two young maids of honor.

There was a moment of silence, then, as the royal group
moved slowly across the gallery, a growing swell of approval
became a roar of acclaim.

The Queen of France followed. Catherine de Médicis
bit her lip. She felt humiliated. The people of France had
never showed her the affection they lavished on her daughter-in-law. With Queen Catherine walked the Prince de
Condé and Henri's sister, Marguerite. Behind them were
the Scottish Queen's grandmother, the Dowager Duchess of
Guise, with the Queen of Navarre and Diane de Poitiers.
Then came many noble ladies of the court, beautifully
gowned. Among them was Mary Stuart's aunt, Anne
d'Este.

The Duc de Guise ordered the nobles who had gathered
on the platform before the doorway of the church to step
back so that the gathered multitude could have a clear view
of the ceremony.

At the entrance to the cathedral, Henri removed from his finger a ring glowing with gems and handed it to the Cardinal de Bourbon, Archbishop of Rouen, signifying that he was chosen to perform the marriage. The Dauphin took his place beside the Queen of Scots under the blue silk canopy. The wedding rites were then performed, and after an eloquent oration by the Bishop of Paris the procession moved up the nave over a carpet of gold cloth to the cathedral to hear the nuptial Mass said.

Outside the church, heralds shouted, "Largesse! Largesse! Largesse!" as they flung gold and silver coins to the crowds. As throngs pushed forward violently to grab for the coins, some cried pitifully to the royal servants to stop for fear they would be trampled to death.

After the church service was completed, Mary Stuart and her husband returned to the Bishop's palace. The air was filled with the shouts of the people and the lively tunes played by the red and yellow attired musicians preceding the newly married couple. In the grand hall, richly decorated for the occasion, a feast arranged by the Duc de Guise awaited them. In compliment to her, the King had commanded two nobles to hold the crown royal above her head as Mary Stuart dined.

At the banquet's end the King of France led a stately dance with his daughter-in-law while the Dauphin politely offered his arm to his mother. Mary Stuart smiled at the gay princess Ysabel dancing with the King of Navarre and her younger sister, Claude, trying to keep up with the Duc de Lorraine.

The Cardinal de Lorraine and the Duc de Guise exchanged pleased glances as they watched their mother's glowing approval of her granddaughter. Diane de Poitiers, too, showed joy in the happiness of her young friend and revealed beyond words her satisfaction in the royal match.

When the dancing stopped, the royal party prepared to leave the Bishop's residence for the Palace of Justice, where elaborate preparation had been made for the evening's festivities.

Mary Stuart rode with Queen Catherine in a silver and red-trimmed open litter. Beside them walked the Cardinal de Lorraine and the Cardinal de Bourbon. The King and Dauphin, mounted on horses with red and silver trappings, rode behind the Queens. Following on gaily bedecked horses were other members of the cortege.

As the procession moved, it was greeted by cheering throngs eager to see their Dauphin's bride. Bargemen doffed their caps and bowed as they glimpsed the colorful group crossing the bridge over the Seine. People shouted from treetops, roofs, and windows. Mary Stuart acknowledged their acclaim with gracious bows and friendly smiles, and with a wave of her hand.

At the palace, the Duc de Guise, in his frosted gold, jewel-embroidered robes, welcomed the wedding party. Proudly he escorted them through the tapestry-walled hall. Hundreds of candles glowed brightly in huge chandeliers. The Duke seated the royal family at a large marble table. Behind them were the statues of the French kings. At other tables arranged for them were the Scottish commissioners, the city fathers in their civic robes, and other honored guests.

The Duc de Guise had managed every detail with the utmost care. Twelve noblemen assisted him to see that everything went smoothly. Magnificently attired pages served savory dishes as the Duke's assistants hovered about the royal family. Soft strains of music floated through the hall.

For the enjoyment of the people, Mary Stuart's uncle had ordered the windows of the hall opened so that those who were fortunate enough to find places on the balconies might see the festivities within.

The young bride looked toward the Dauphin and smiled. He seemed bewildered at the fast-moving pomp and ceremony.

More dancing followed the banquet. The King once more led the ball with his daughter-in-law, and the Dauphin danced again with his mother.

Elaborate masques, mummeries, and other pastimes had been planned for the evening, for the Duc de Guise had spared no expense to honor his niece. He and the Cardinal had vowed that the wedding would be the most resplendent of all time. Scotland might pay for it, but the House of Guise would be remembered for it.

When the dancing was over, the entertainment began. The spectators beheld a series of planets unfolding before their eyes as a winged Mercury in white satin with a golden girdle, caduceus in his hand, stepped into their midst. Mars followed in costly armor, and Venus in soft flowing draperies. There was an interlude of music and then a parade of lackeys leading wicker hobby horses each bearing a royal prince. Behind them a train of coaches carried a group of silver- and gold-clad pilgrims singing hymns and psalms of praise to the newly married pair. Then came two beautiful white steeds drawing a chariot with the nine Muses.

Mary Stuart could hardly believe her eyes as the next display appeared. Breathlessly she stared as six ships propelled by some unseen device sailed slowly across the ballroom floor as though they were on a rolling sea. Each ship was of cloth of gold and crimson velvet, and each was

manned by a masked prince arrayed in gold. Beside each
royal mariner was an empty chair waiting for his princess
to occupy it.

The ships approached the marble table where the ladies
were seated and came to a stop. Then, much to the delight
of the audience, King Henri, masked and clothed like the
other princes, drew Mary Stuart to the empty chair beside
him. The Dauphin seated his mother, Queen Catherine, at
his side; the Duc de Lorraine chose Princess Claude; the
King of Navarre, his Queen, the Duc de Nemours took the
King's sister, Madame Marguerite, and the Prince de Condé,
the Duchesse de Guise. To the strains of soft music the
ships set sail again. The Cardinal wondered if the future
held a calmer or stormier sea for the royal pair. At least for
the moment the Guises had weathered all storms. This
marriage was the pinnacle of their success.

As dawn broke, the festivities came to an end. The
happy but weary Mary Stuart and François, together with
the royal family, retired to the Palace of the Tournelles.

Chapter Twelve

While bonfires burned throughout Scotland in honor of the Queen's marriage, and France continued to celebrate the wedding for three days more, the royal couple went with a select few to Villers-Cotterêts to spend their honeymoon. Mary Stuart was well acquainted with this residence of the Guises. She knew its vast forests and parks from the days when the Cardinal had brought her there to shield her from Madame de Paroy.

This time she and François could arrange their lives to suit themselves. There was no governess for her, or governor for him. As the days swiftly followed one another the two young people found nothing to mar their delight. Mary Stuart took joy in the awareness that François depended on her to plan for them both. She was pleased that he also turned to her uncles, the Cardinal de Lorraine, and the Duc de Guise for counsel. She loved it when François wandered into her rooms to watch and admire, or just to be with her as she continued her studies: Latin with George Buchanan, history with Monsieur de Pasquier, and poetry with her friend, Pierre de Ronsard.

Mary Stuart would never forget François' childlike delight when he saw the coin bearing both their likenesses that Henri had had struck in honor of their marriage. She ordered a similar one to be fashioned by the Scottish royal mint.

The young Queen enjoyed the hunts in which they both took part. Despite his frailness the Dauphin rode well; and

she was proud of his fearless horsemanship. He had become interested in *jeu de paume* as well, and when she
suggested going to the pleasure court for a game, François
eagerly accompanied her. He was not as quick as she would
have wished, but his enthusiastic efforts helped her to over-
look his slowness. The evening hours spent with the ladies
and gentlemen of their court dancing or listening to their
musicians were happy ones. Often François proudly asked
Mary Stuart to sing and accompany herself on the lute.

Mary Stuart wished they would never have to leave Villers-Cotterêts, where they had found such happiness. François agreed. If they could only go on like this forever.

All too soon a message came from the King informing
François that the time had come for him to acquire some
skill in arms and knowledge of how to lead men in battle.
Mary Stuart was as distressed as was François. But at least
it was her warrior uncle, the Duc de Guise, under whose
guidance François would serve his military apprenticeship.
Her uncle would see that no harm befell him. Sadly the
two young people parted. They had been married three
months.

A month later the Scottish commissioners came to pay
their respects to their Queen before returning to Scotland.
Mary Stuart instructed them, in accord with the terms of
the marriage contract, to request the Estates to send the
Scottish crown to France, so that her husband, already
granted the title of King of Scotland, might be crowned
with it.

Toward the end of October, while the Scottish Queen
remained at Villers-Cotterêts trying to shut out her loneliness, Henri was at Cercamp endeavoring to bring about
peace between France, Spain, and England. But the negotiations were brought to an abrupt end by the death of

England's Queen, Mary Tudor, on November 17, 1558. Mary Tudor's efforts to bring England back into the Roman Catholic fold were doomed by the accession to the throne of Elizabeth Tudor, the twenty-five-year-old daughter of Henri VIII and Anne Boleyn.

The Cardinal hurried to Mary Stuart. She must be made to realize that it was she, daughter of James V of Scotland and great-granddaughter of Henry VII of England, who was the rightful heir to the English throne. She must know that in the eyes of the Roman Catholic world Anne Boleyn's marriage to Henry VIII was invalid, which meant they recognized no heir in the direct line of succession. By this reasoning Elizabeth Tudor was an illegitimate child and had no legal right to succeed Mary Tudor.

The French King was as eager as Mary Stuart's uncles to have the great-granddaughter of Henry VII proclaimed Queen of England, Scotland, and Ireland. Henri requested the Cardinal to instruct his daughter-in-law to affix this title to her documents. Both she and François would have the arms of England embroidered on their heraldic banners and engraved on their plate. Both he and the Cardinal knew that, although Elizabeth professed to be a Roman Catholic, at heart she was a Protestant, biding her time to establish the new doctrines in England as her father had done. The reform leaders would find easy ways to undermine the Roman Catholic Church in Scotland with their tainted money. France, too, already had its share of heretics, the Huguenots. From what his spies were able to detect, Henri thought his country would be overrun with them if he were not careful.

The Cardinal watched his niece's face as he explained in detail every reason why Mary Stuart had the right to the throne of England. He emphasized that her religion should not be imperiled by one who was actually a usurper.

Mary Stuart listened carefully. Her uncle, the Duc de Guise, and the King had never failed to support her mother or Scotland. They had helped to preserve her realm. They had done everything for her happiness and well-being. She had always abided by their wishes. She would do so now, not because she wished to acquire the English throne, but in order to have Roman Catholicism prevail.

Elizabeth Tudor was crowned Queen of England in Westminster Abbey on January 15, 1559. In France, the talk of wars, thrones, and religion was forgotten for the time being. Princess Claude, twelve-year-old daughter of Henri, was to be married to the young Duc de Lorraine on the twenty-second of January in the Cathedral of Notre-Dame in Paris. Mary Stuart was elated, not only for her former playmate, but because it brought François home again.

Sixteen-year-old Mary Stuart drew as much acclaim from the people as she walked in Princess Claude's wedding procession as she had in her own nine months earlier. The foreign dignitaries smiled smugly to themselves when they saw the arms of England conspicuously displayed with the Dauphin's. One of them wrote: "Whatever they shall say, sing or pipe, their interest is to increase the power of their niece the Queen of Scots and her posterity, which will be the chief staff and pillar that the house of Guise will have to trust to. And for this what could they wish for more than that England might be brought under France by the Queen of Scots' feigned title to the crown of England?"

Mary Stuart was glad when the festivities were over. They had seemed endless. Neither she nor the Dauphin had felt well. She would be happy when they were in their own household. These had been demanding and wearying days.

While Mary Stuart and François enjoyed the quiet of their own court, the peace negotiations were resumed at Cambrai. The English demanded the restoration of Calais. The French representatives retorted, "In that case, it ought to be surrendered to the Dauphin's consort, the Queen of Scots, whom we take to be the Queen of England." Elizabeth Tudor never forgave this insult.

The ink was scarcely dry on the peace treaty which had finally been signed at Cateau-Cambrésis on April 2, 1559 between England, France, and Spain with Mary Stuart and François among the signatories for France, when Elizabeth Tudor's agents were on their way to Scotland. They were far more adept than the men who had worked for her father, and it was not long before the Queen of Scots was reading evil tidings of unrest and dissension in letters from her mother. If only Mary Stuart could do something to help. As the news grew more distressing, the young Queen's health was undermined, and she became so ill that frequently she had to be carried half-fainting from church, the banquet hall, or a court ball.

As part of the peace treaty, Mary Stuart's favorite sister-in-law, Ysabel, was promised in marriage to Philip II of Spain, the widower of Mary Tudor. He was thirty-two, and Ysabel was fourteen. The pact also betrothed Henri's sister, Princess Marguerite, to Emmanuel Philibert de Savoie. The Duc de Savoie would arrive soon for his wedding. Ysabel was to be married by proxy; the Duc d'Albe would represent his royal master.

The time drew near when the wedding was to take place. Frightened and lonely, Ysabel wrote begging Mary Stuart

and François to be with her. She dreaded marrying someone so much older, leaving France, parting from her beloved sisters and brothers and, of course, Mary Stuart.

The Queen of Scots shook off her illness enough to make
the journey. It was not a happy time—nothing like the
joyous preparations for her marriage to François. She tried
to comfort the disheartened Ysabel. There would be letters, she told her, frequent ones, full of news, and there
would be visits from the royal family.

The King of France was determined that his eldest
daughter's wedding should be a dazzling celebration. Days
of gala entertainment and a three-day tournament were to
conclude the nuptials and the final acceptance of the peace
treaty.

On June twenty-second, Henri and his court, the foreign
dignitaries and royal guests heard the proxy marriage of
Ysabel solemnized in the Cathedral of Notre-Dame.

After six days of elaborate masques, pageants, and court
balls, the tournament began. Rich and poor, high and low
hurried each morning to fill every available space around
the tilting yard, with its colored pennants and gay tents
erected for the King and his guests. On the final day of the
tournament the King himself planned to enter the lists. All
eyes were upon the mounted horsemen. They rode into the
yard escorted by a band playing lively music. Among the
ladies were Queen Catherine, the King's sister, Marguerite,
and Diane de Poitiers. Yet it was none of these three who
caught all eyes, but Mary Stuart. The royal litter which
bore her to her place was conspicuously decorated with the
arms of England, Scotland and Ireland, and with those of
France. Upon the arches below the balcony where she, the
Dauphin, and their escort would sit were these Scottish
verses:

"The Armes of Mary Queen Dolphin of France,
The noblest Lady in Earth for till avance,
    Of Scotland Queen and England too,
    Of Ireland too, as God hath provided it so."

But Mary Stuart could not keep her eyes off Catherine.
Never had she seen the Queen so distressed. Turning to
Nurse Sinclair, Mary Stuart asked if she, too, had noticed
the Queen's manner. The faithful servant explained that
the Queen had been wakened from her sleep the night before by a fearful dream in which she saw her husband slain
by a lance which pierced his eye.

The young Queen looked sympathetically at her mother-
in-law, knowing how seriously she took her dreams. No
wonder the poor woman seemed so worried. The Queen,
Mary Stuart reasoned, could relax now. The King already
had tilted three times, and with his usual skill and vigor
he had broken the lances of his opponents. Mary Stuart
was glad that François had come unscathed through his
joust.

The Scottish Queen turned in surprise as Henri entered
their pavilion with the Dauphin. She had never seen the
King so flushed with excitement. The Dauphin showed
signs of fatigue.

She watched the King. More and more she sensed his
impatience and restlessness as he saw riders unhorsed and
heard lances split. She was not surprised when he hurried
toward his tent. Mary Stuart turned in time to see a mes-
senger leave Queen Catherine. Nurse Sinclair guessed that
the Queen had sent word to the King beseeching him not
to go into the lists again.

A few moments later, Mary Stuart knew Queen Catherine's message had gone unheeded. She saw the King
emerge from his tent in his armor wearing the black and

white colors of Diane de Poitiers. Raising his visor for the moment he mounted his black charger, Le Malheureux. An attendant handed him a lance.

Trumpets sounded, drawing all eyes to the end of the field. As vigorous as if he had just begun, the King rode forward amidst thundering shouts to meet the Comte de Montgomery, Captain of the Scottish Guard, the only man who had accepted his challenge. He would show that he still had the strength of youth. What were three times in the field to a man like himself!

Mary Stuart tried to quell her uneasiness. Suppose Queen Catherine's dream . . . The King and Montgomery took their places at the correct distance. Now they exchanged the customary salutes.

A breathless silence came over the spectators. The Scottish Queen glanced at the Dauphin. He was pale and rigid. She heard heavy breathing and felt the tension around her, as the King and the Captain rode toward each other with lances extended. Fists clenched, Mary Stuart leaned forward. The contestants were closer—their lances raised— they missed! Again the riders circled the lists and charged, only to miss again. Mary Stuart wiped the perspiration from her forehead as Henri and the Captain came toward one another for the third time. On they galloped. Would they miss again . . . Would . . .

Mary Stuart's hands went to her ears. Montgomery's lance splintered again at the King's casque. Henri reeled, and a roar of applause filled the air as he steadied himself and remained horsed. But the acclaim died out as quickly as it had come. The King had fallen forward on his horse. Queen Catherine screamed as attendants rushed to catch their monarch, then swooned as she saw her husband's blood stream from his head and face when his helmet was removed. The point of Montgomery's lance had lifted the King's visor and pierced his eye.

Mary Stuart cried out in horror—Nurse Sinclair covered her face—the Dauphin fainted. Diane de Poitiers tried to force her way through the jostling crowds, but was shoved back to be carried away from her beloved King.

Writhing with pain the French King was carried into the Palace of the Tournelles. For ten days he hovered between life and death, with the ablest physicians in attendance. Philip II sent his own surgeon, the renowned Vesalius, posthaste to Paris.

None but his family and a few faithful old friends were permitted to enter Henri's chambers. Diane de Poitiers sought to see him but Queen Catherine refused her admittance. Diane de Poitiers had deprived the Queen of many happy days with her husband. She would not share his last hours. At first Mary Stuart and the Dauphin were frequent visitors to the royal bedchamber. But as the King grew worse the Dauphin could not bear the sight, and broke under the strain. Mary Stuart remained with François. Her husband needed all the comfort and help she had to give him.

Henri's courageous fight, all the medical skill, and even the prayers of the people who crowded the guarded palace gates were unavailing. On July 10, 1559, eleven days after the fateful joust, in the thirteenth year of his reign, Henri II, King of France, breathed his last.

The Paris that had been so gay was now a city of gloom. But it would not last. There was another King to be crowned soon, Mary Stuart's husband, François II.

Chapter Thirteen

In her apartments at Blois, seven months later, seventeen-year-old Mary Stuart looked up from her embroidery. As she watched François struggling with a document the Cardinal had left for him to study, her mind ran quickly over the events of the last half year.

At her suggestion, François had named the Cardinal minister for civil, financial, and foreign affairs. Her other uncle, the Duc de Guise, had taken over the management of the army. The Guises had appointed men they could trust to help administer the affairs of France. But François still had to make some decisions and it was only right that she should help with them. She dropped her embroidery and went over to the table.

She had shouldered many responsibilities for her husband. François had come to her soon after his accession. He needed help. He did not want to be the one to tell his father's aging friend and Minister of State, the Constable de Montmorency, that the affairs of his kingdom were now to be entrusted to Mary Stuart's uncles. When she pointed out to François that matters would be simpler if he accepted her uncles' advice, he no longer hesitated to dismiss the Constable.

She had raised no objection when Catherine de Médicis, now the Queen Dowager of France, had besought her son to appoint her Queen Regent. The widow had shown great sympathy and devotion to François since the day of Henri's fatal accident. After years of aloofness, she had begun to show some affection for Mary Stuart. The young Queen had only compassion for her mother-in-law, whose tears still flowed at the mention of Henri.

François' mother had promised not to ally herself with the Bourbon princes or any faction opposed to her son's government. She had approved François' appointment of the Cardinal and the Duc de Guise to their new offices.

But in spite of all this cooperation Mary Stuart's uncles warned their niece that the Queen Dowager's ingratiating manner and affable words were only tricks to gain favor with the King and the Queen. She wanted to rule France through them if she could do it no other way. To do that she must crush the power of the Guises. Her uncles had accepted the King's appointment of his mother because they were aware that she would be Regent only in name. They advised Mary Stuart to treat the Queen Regent with respect and kindness, but never to become subject to her influence. Both she and François must consult her uncles before making any important decisions.

Seated now beside her husband, Mary Stuart read the papers. François brightened as she explained the text. Mary Stuart realized the Cardinal had composed it to give the King the feeling that he was actually taking part in the government of his realm.

While François continued to study, Mary Stuart looked with pleasure at the Great Seal lying on the table. It depicted herself and her husband, royal-robed and seated on separate thrones under a canopy dotted with fleurs-de-lis. Each wore a crown and held a sceptre. The Queen glowed as she read the words *"Franciscus et Maria, Dei Gratia Franciae, Scotiae, Angliae, et Hiberniae Rex et Regina"* on the obverse of the Great Seal which had been issued by the Paris mint shortly after the late King's death.

The Queen smiled as she thought of the objections Sir Nicholas Throckmorton, the English ambassador, had raised to the use of the arms of England on her banners at François' coronation the previous October. His annoyance had continued when he saw them conspicuously displayed on the long tour the court had made after the coronation. At court banquets Elizabeth Tudor's representative ate from plates bearing the same arms. She remembered the delight with which she and her uncles had watched his face.

As she thought back to François' coronation, the Queen's face flushed. It had been a dismal day, rainy and windy, and the ceremony had been equally depressing. Out of respect to his father, François had ordered all the ladies to wear plain black silk or velvet dresses and no jewels. Mary Stuart was the only exception. She wore white with sparkling jewels and a sable train. Despite the gloom, it was the greatest day of François' life—the day when he became King of France and Mary Stuart his Queen Consort. The crowds had cheered him as he rode his beautiful white charger; when the Queen followed him into Reims their shouts were deafening. As the court journeyed from place to place they were greeted in the same manner. If François resented the overwhelming acclaim for the Queen, he never showed it, but continued waving and smiling sincerely.

Mary Stuart looked at François, still bent over his task. His people could no longer call him "*le petit roi.*" He had grown taller in these past months. But she was concerned, for he was paler and thinner. Both she and François had been critically ill several times while on their way to Blois.

As the court had neared its journey's end, a story had reached the people that their King had an incurable disease. Seeking to avoid contagion, the peasants had completely deserted the countryside. Mary Stuart knew how deeply humiliated François was. They had both rejoiced when people again appeared to greet them. The story was no longer believed.

She would never forget how distressed François had been when she was thrown from her horse while hunting. The King had embraced her and had wept at intervals for days at the thought of her nearly having been trampled. For a time he would not let her out of his sight, and when they hunted, François insisted that he ride beside her.

Mary Stuart realized that her illness had come from anxiety over the news from her mother. Mary of Guise was not well, and Scotland was overrun with heretics who pillaged and destroyed her abbeys and churches. The same John Knox who had preached against Roman Catholicism over thirteen years ago was back from Calvanist Geneva and was rousing the people again. While pretending to be a friend of Scotland and France, Elizabeth Tudor was aiding the Protestant leaders in Scotland and the Huguenots in France.

The startling word that the heir apparent to the Scottish throne, the Duc de Châtelherault, his son the Earl of Arran, and her half-brother, the Lord James Stuart, had joined the insurgents made Mary Stuart take to her bed. She would not believe that her nobles had allied themselves with the Protestants because they found a threat to Scotland's independence in French control of the principal offices and some of the strongholds of her realm.

Despite the animosity of her nobles and their fear that Scotland would become a French dependency, Mary Stuart begged François and the Cardinal to send more military aid to her mother to help crush the insurgents. Both the King and her uncle had responded to her wishes.

Mary Stuart looked around the beautifully paneled room with its great fireplace. Blois held happy memories for her. She and her mother had spent much of their time together here. Blois, too, was the scene of that exciting moment when Henri had given her her first horses, Bravane and Madame la Réale, and had presented François with Fontaine. She would always remember her rides through the forest and the exciting hunts with Diane de Poitiers.

Mary Stuart roused herself. François had worked long enough. She would send for the Lady Marys, Nurse Sinclair, and John Kemp. They would all go to see François' new hunting dogs. Why not make it a gala event and take Princes Charles, Edouard Alexandre, and Princess Marguerite? Prince Hercule was still too small to walk that distance. Mary Stuart paused. If Ysabel and Claude were only here to go with them too! She had missed Ysabel of late. She knew Claude was happy with the young Duc de Lorraine, but she often wondered about Ysabel. King Philip II of Spain was so much older than his youthful wife. . . .

In her apartments above those of the royal couple the Queen Mother drew aside the drapery at her window. Her thick lips smiled as she watched the King and Queen and their party crossing the courtyard below. She prided herself on her skill in making François and Mary Stuart believe that her affection for them was genuine. But how could it be? Ever since François' marriage, his eyes, ears, and words were only for the girl Queen who had captured the heart of France.

The Queen Mother narrowed her dark eyes. Could the Guises know that she had never meant her pledge to support them? Ever since the English Queen had sent aid to the Bourbon princes who now were linked with the Huguenot movement against the Catholic royal family, Catherine de Médicis had been allied with them. She was in constant communication with the Prince de Condé, one of their principal leaders. The Bourbon's confidence was hers, and soon—the Queen Mother gloated, it could not come too soon—the Guises would no longer rule. The government would be in the hands of the Huguenots, and she would be head of their Council, wielding power in her own name. She would go now and consult her horoscope.

Chapter Fourteen

Mary Stuart and François had just returned to their chambers from the royal kennels, when the Cardinal was ushered in. The Queen drew back as she looked upon her uncle's agitated face and terror-filled eyes. Was there more bad news from Scotland?

The Cardinal wasted no time on formalities. Blois was no longer safe for the royal family. A plot had been discovered. The Huguenots, led by the Bourbon princes, were planning to surround the château a week or ten days hence. The King and Queen were to be imprisoned in separate fortresses. The Cardinal and the Duc de Guise were to be sent to the scaffold.

Hasty preparations were made to take the royal household at once to Amboise. On its high rock above the river the château could be well fortified. Should the rebels follow as far as Amboise, the Duc de Guise and his troops would be ready to oppose them. The royal procession would go forth just as it always did when moving from one château to another, so as not to rouse suspicion. The King would ride; the Queen and her ladies would go in litters, the Queen Mother in her coach. There was nothing to fear if they went at once. The procession would be well protected. The Duke's soldiers were already in hiding along the route.

Mary Stuart was stunned. Then she reached to steady François as he sank into a chair, gasping pitifully. "What have I done to displease my people? I listen to their petitions, and desire to perform my duty to them."

Before the Cardinal could reply, François was on his feet. "I have heard," said the King, pointing a shaking finger at the prelate, "that it is you, gentlemen, who cause disaffection: I wish you would leave me to myself, and we should soon see whether the blow is aimed at you or at me."

The Queen was astounded. François talking like this to the Cardinal! François must be ill—very ill. She must stop him. She started to move but hesitated as her uncle humbled himself on his knees saying, "Ah, Sire! If our retreat would satisfy your enemies, we should not hesitate to withdraw; but it is religion," the Cardinal continued quietly but deliberately, "it is the throne—it is France itself, they wish to subvert. All these are menaced by the Huguenots, whose aim is to destroy the royal family, and to transform France into a republic. Such is the object of this conspiracy. Will you abandon your faithful servants? Will you abandon yourself?" The voice was low but compelling.

François' eyes smarted. Laying his hand gently on the Cardinal's shoulder, the shaken King bade the Queen's uncle to rise, and embraced him. The Guises would carry on for the French government as long as François II lived. The royal household would move to Amboise as the Cardinal planned.

The Cardinal started to withdraw but hesitated. No one else knew the conspiracy had been discovered. No one else must know—not even the Queen Mother. The Cardinal's voice softened. She must be spared that agony at the moment. She had suffered enough since the King's passing. The Cardinal looked his compassion as he talked. He was not ready to let the King and Queen know Catherine de Médicis' part in the plot.

How would the Queen Mother feel about the move, the Cardinal wondered, as he paused at the stairway leading to her apartments. She could not protest when he told her that the King had given him authority to move the court. He must not intimate the reason now but, once settled at Amboise, he would make it his immediate business to warn her of the plot. The Queen Mother must never suspect that he was aware of her connection with the Huguenot conspiracy. The Cardinal hurried up the steps to Queen Catherine's chambers. What were spies for? The Queen Mother would have to be watched more closely from now on. . . .

As her horses climbed the hill to the court's fortress home, Mary Stuart prayed that Amboise would hold them but a short time. There were so many more attractive royal châteaux where she would rather be. From her mother she had learned that her life in Scotland had been one flight after another. This, Mary Stuart was thankful to admit, was her first in France. The last one, she hoped.

Both Mary Stuart and François were glad that they were on the last lap of the journey. Soon they would be able to relax. The tension had been nerve-racking.

At their apartments in Amboise, François handed his wife her lute to accompany the song she was to sing for him. Scarcely had Mary Stuart begun when the Queen Mother and the Cardinal were announced.

At once Mary Stuart sensed her mother-in-law's uneasiness. Had the Queen Mother had another one of her premonitions, she wondered. Her uncle had eyes for the Queen Mother only, as she commenced to speak. The Queen Mother's comment on the Cardinal's news of the Huguenots treacherous conspiracy was distressing. She was touched, Catherine de Médicis blinked back a forced tear, that to shield her from grief Mary Stuart and François had borne the burden of the knowledge of the plot. Had the King and Queen felt any ill effects from the journey? The Cardinal, she continued, had told her there was no further cause to be alarmed for their safety. Every door and passageway was guarded. She hoped the King and Queen would soon be enjoying the freedom of the hunts and other outdoor activities. While they were at Amboise she would help to make their stay pleasant. There would be musicals, masques, dances, and . . .

Puzzled, Mary Stuart stared. She had never known her mother-in-law to be so solicitous. The Queen glanced at her uncle. Above a cynical smile their eyes met. Mary Stuart was astonished at her thoughts. Was Queen Catherine really serious or was this a subterfuge to cover up some clever scheme?

The Court had been at Amboise but a short time when the English ambassador, Throckmorton, paid Mary Stuart a visit. In the presence of the Queen Mother he made known Elizabeth Tudor's desire to maintain the friendship between France and England. To this Mary Stuart replied pointedly, "Yes, the Queen my good sister may be assured to have a better neighbor of me, being her cousin, than of the rebels, and so pray I you signify unto her."

It was shocking to Mary Stuart that only two days after the English ambassador's visit she was again the recipient of heartbreaking news from Scotland. Elizabeth Tudor had concluded a treaty at Berwick with the Lords of the Congregation promising to protect Scotland's rights and liberties against French domination. Mary Stuart was well aware that such a treaty meant military assistance from England. Her mother would need reinforcements from France.

Scotland must not become Protestant. Yet this was inevitable if her government was controlled by the Lords of the Congregation.

Mary Stuart's mind was in a turmoil. Whom could she believe? Whom could she trust, with intrigue all around her? What were peace treaties for if they were not to be kept?

Tension and fear mounted in the court. Each day told of Huguenot traitors captured, imprisoned, and executed.

As March wore on the situation became acute. The Cardinal's terror-stricken eyes, his restlessness, his quick temper and his ever-watching manner frightened Mary Stuart. Had the Cardinal exaggerated the Duc de Guise's strength? Was the royal army strong enough to prevent the Huguenots from taking Amboise? Amboise in the hands of the insurgents would mean imprisonment for her and François. She could not bear to think of it, yet she could not blot it from her mind. And why was François' mother constantly urging her son to show more mercy to the Huguenot prisoners who were trying to ursurp his throne and imprison him and his wife? Why? Why? Mary Stuart kept asking herself.

Toward the end of March, the woods at Amboise rang unexpectedly with clashing steel, piercing screams, breaking branches, and stampeding horses.

The clamor penetrated the massive walls of the château. Mary Stuart was not well but she tried to bolster her courage. If only she had the strength to comfort the weeping Princess Marguerite and the Princes Edouard Alexandre and Hercule who huddled in a corner at the far end of the room. Prince Charles, evidently delighted with the thought of war and excitement, clung to his place at the window. Gratefully Mary Stuart noted that the four Lady Marys shielded François from the scene below. If only the Queen Mother would take her baleful eyes off her and François. . . .

There was quiet now in the woods. The royal chambers were tense and still as the tumult died. Then triumphant cheers brought the royal family to their feet. Mary Stuart turned to ask the Cardinal what this meant, then realized he had slipped away unnoticed. The Queen Mother was the first to move to the windowed balcony. Mary Stuart gasped when she saw her mother-in-law turn pale then sway. But the woman was quick to compose herself and hastily beckoned the King and Queen. Flinging open the windowed doors the Queen Mother stepped onto the balcony.

Mary Stuart's heart was heavy as she and François responded to his mother's summons. Had the Cardinal become a victim of the Huguenots? Had no one thought that the shouting men might not be the King's?

As though in a trance Mary Stuart reached the Queen Mother as the Duc de Guise in the courtyard below bellowed the word for the executions to begin. Mary Stuart screamed and fainted. François drew back, crying out to stay the slaughter, but his wails were lost in the din as his mother forced him forward again to watch. These were the men in whose hands she had hoped he would be this day. What a fiasco this plot had been—and how fortunate for her that her part in it was undiscovered!

The Queen Mother lingered. She seethed that the Bourbon Prince de Condé was not among the lifeless bodies lying on the ground. While leading a preliminary skirmish several days before, that leader had deserted his own men to fight with the King's troops when he found the Huguenots were outnumbered. Obviously Condé was not to be trusted. She had been warned that he was merely using her as a tool. Once he and the Bourbons had control of François' government, it was Condé, not the Queen Mother, who would seize all power.

The Dauphin's mother took a deep breath; she must go now and see to her son's frail Queen. For a while yet Catherine de Médicis must still play up to her daughter-in-law, her son, and the Guises. She patted François' shoulder as she brushed by the distracted King. The Guises had been victorious this time, but the Huguenots would not forget the Tumult of Amboise of March, 1560.

Chapter Fifteen

As soon as the young Queen had recovered from the shock of the Huguenot massacre, the court moved to peaceful Chenonceaux. Here in the palatial château built over the river Cher, Mary Stuart slowly blotted out the memory of the executioner's ax and the hangman's rope.

But the Queen and her husband had just begun to enjoy both the court activities and the occasional hunts in the adjoining woods when she became ill again. Civil war had swept through Scotland. Mary of Guise was virtually a prisoner in Edinburgh Castle, but despite her growing illness the Dowager Queen had rallied her remaining supporters and the French troops in their fight to preserve Roman Catholicism and her daughter's realm. In spite of this the Queen Regent's health and her position steadily grew weaker. Mary Stuart's mother lacked supplies, arms, and men.

Scotland was beginning to feel the effects of the Cardinal's advice to his niece regarding her rights to the English throne. Elizabeth Tudor had issued a public proclamation justifying her intervention in that troubled land, declaring:

"that the injurious pretences made by the Queen of Scots to this realm proceed from the principals of the house of Guise, who now have the chief governance of the crown of France, and that neither the French King (who by reason of his years is not capable of such an

119

enterprise) nor the Queen of Scots, his wife, (also being in her minority), nor yet the Princes of the blood royal and other estates of France, have imagined such an unjust enterprise. The house of Guise, for their private advancement exalting their niece, the Queen of Scots, have thus injuriously set forth and in time of peace continued in public the arms of England and Ireland in the name of their niece; and have used the authority of the King and Queen to enterprise the eviction of the crown of Scotland out of the power of the natural people of the land, and thereby to proceed with force, meaning to invade England. The Queen, being desirous to keep peace with all, notifies that she is forced to put in order, to her great charge, certain forces by sea and land for the safeguard of England."

Mary Stuart besought her uncles, the King, and even the Queen Mother for additional aid for Mary of Guise. As much assistance as could be given was promised. Encouraged, the Scottish Queen wrote to her mother:

"François has so much care to aid you that you will be content with him, for he has thus promised me, and I will not let him forget it, nor the Queen Mother either who has honored us by weeping copiously upon hearing your troubles. I have urged her so that I am sure that she will not fail to send you all the help that she can."

Restless and distracted during the spring months, Mary Stuart moved with the court from one château to another. Couriers from Scotland brought continuous disheartening messages: that her realm was in desperate straits, and that Mary of Guise's health grew steadily worse. The Guises appealed in vain for foreign assistance. France could no longer spare men, arms, or supplies; her treasury was low and the King's soldiers were needed to prevent the Huguenots from overthrowing the government.

In her anguish Mary Stuart refused comfort from her uncles, the Queen Mother, or even her beloved François. Aimlessly she paced her chambers or took to her bed with weeping. Lamenting over her mother's ill health and the deplorable state of her country, the Scottish Queen turned upon her uncles, exclaiming that they had undone her, and caused her to lose her realm.

On June 10, 1560, while her daughter moved with the court to Saint-Germain-en-Laye, Mary of Guise lay dying in Edinburgh Castle. She bade farewell to a few friends at her bedside, and then closed her eyes for the last time.

The Cardinal was the first to learn of the tragic event. Tears coursed down his cheeks as he read the eight-day-old message. He had really loved his forty-five-year-old sister. She had stood for all that the Guises could have hoped for; she had been a devoted mother, faithful and dauntless. She had been an ardent adherent to the Roman Catholic Church. The responsibilities of her daughter's realm had never been neglected, nor had she overlooked her allegiance to France.

But it was not so much his sister's death or the awareness that Scotland was already in the hands of the Lords of the Congregation that troubled the Cardinal, as the problem of how he would break the news to his niece. Her health had already been impaired by the horrors of Amboise, her mother's illness, the disordered conditions of her realm, and her recently shattered faith in her uncle's management of her affairs in Scotland.

The Cardinal decided that she could not stand the shock.

He would keep the message a secret for the time being. Meanwhile, he must carry the sorrowful news to his aging mother, the Dowager Duchess of Guise. Perhaps his mother would return with him to Saint-Germain-en-Laye when she had recovered from his doleful visit.

In her apartments ten days later Mary Stuart rose to greet her grandmother and uncle. Compassion swept over her as she saw the Cardinal's drawn face. Perhaps she had been too hasty in reproaching her uncles so bitterly. She must be kinder, more considerate. And her dear grand-mother—how sad she seemed. Was she still mourning the loss of her husband, Claude, or had something happened to her warrior son, the Duc de Guise—or—no—it could not be—it *must* not be—her mother!

When she heard the news, she was plunged into the deepest grief she had yet experienced. Mary Stuart was oblivious to the consolation offered her by any one, even François. Her beloved mother was gone—gone forever. She had been so alone, without any member of her own family during those last hours. Although Mary Stuart had known her mother was ill, she had not been aware that her condition was so severe. If only she could have seen her again—just once.

As the heartbroken Queen passed from one grief to another she ceased to cry, and gradually she came to a clear realization of her mother's courage and strength. The sense of death lifted; Mary Stuart controlled her sorrow. She began to relive some of her memories of her mother.

She remembered the day she and her mother had watched the ships anchored in the Clyde below Dumbarton Castle, ships that would carry Mary Stuart to France. She could almost hear her mother's strong and gentle voice as she told of all the things her daughter would do and see there.

Mary Stuart had never forgotten her mother's saying that some day she, like her father, would rule Scotland. She was a Queen, and much was expected of a Queen—

She smiled through her swollen eyes at François as she reached for his hand. François looked so thin, so forlorn. He wanted to comfort her. She must give her husband more of herself. François needed her and she needed him. Scotland needed them both.

With the death of Mary of Guise the cause of France in Scotland was definitely lost. Much against their wills, François and Mary Stuart participated in the negotiations for peace.

With mounting indignation they read the terms of the Treaty of Edinburgh drawn up and signed by the Scots and the English on July 6, 1560. The English had gained exactly what they wanted. No longer would Scotland be a pawn of France. The French were to withdraw all but one hundred and twenty soldiers. Fortifications at Leith were to be demolished. No foreigners were to hold high office, and no financial office was to be entrusted to a cleric. Mary Stuart and her French husband no longer were to use the arms of England and Ireland. Until the Queen of Scots returned to her realm, the Scottish Estates were to select twenty-four persons from whom Mary Stuart would appoint seven, and the Estates five, to compose a council of twelve. Neither Mary Stuart nor François would be permitted to order peace or war in Scotland without the consent of the Scottish Estates.

Mary Stuart declared she never would accept the Treaty of Edinburgh, or renounce her rights to the English throne. Nor would she agree to remove what was legally hers, the arms of England and Ireland. Scotland had its place in the

world and so did its Queen. Let Elizabeth Tudor and her
secretaries and ambassadors plot and plan! Mary Stuart
was the daughter of Mary of Guise and James V; she
would bide her time until she was ready to act.

But it was not long before the Scottish Queen's confidence and determination were severely shaken. Early in
August she learned that the Scottish Parliament had
abolished Roman Catholicism and the jurisdiction of the
Pope in Scotland. It had declared further that, if anyone
heard or said Mass, the first offense would be punishable
by confiscation of possessions, the second would bring
banishment, and the third, death.

Mary Stuart was in despair. Without France's aid the
cause of the Roman Catholic Church in Scotland was
doomed.

Dressed in mourning, the King and his court accompanied the Queen on August twelfth to attend the services
for her mother in the Cathedral of Notre-Dame. Touched
by the oration made by the learned and kindly Claude
d'Espence of the Sorbonne, Mary of Guise's daughter
found strength to fight for the Roman Catholic Church in
Scotland.

Chapter Sixteen

The Scottish war over, Mary Stuart's uncles turned their attention to problems at home. The Huguenots were spreading rapidly in France and causing serious trouble in the provinces. The Guises found themselves constantly under attack. Vicious pamphlets and papers disparaging the Cardinal were circulated, and he was hanged in effigy several times. Neither of Mary Stuart's uncles now went anywhere without a bodyguard. Beneath their garments, it was rumored, they wore shirts of chain mail.

The Guises were aware that an accounting of some kind would have to be made. They could not permit the French Protestants to gain the same footing that the Protestants had in Scotland and in England. A meeting of notables was called for the latter part of August at Fontainebleau. The royal family and the Guises hoped that a public airing of grievances and dissatisfactions on this occasion would lead to a mutually satisfactory solution.

Mary Stuart was proud of François as he rose to open the Assembly. But as she watched him she was troubled—how thin, how tired he looked. She hoped that he was not going to be ill again. After the meeting they would go to one of their quieter châteaux to rest and enjoy a simpler life.

As the session progressed, Mary Stuart could hardly believe her ears. The Roman Catholic Bishop of Valence, who had just returned from Scotland, was advocating Protestantism, upbraiding the Roman Catholic clergy, and proposing to the King that he and his household should hear a Protestant sermon daily. Mary Stuart wanted to bury her head in her hands and weep when the prelate boldly addressed her and the Queen Mother saying, "Pardon me if I presume to entreat that you will be pleased to ordain that, instead of foolish songs, your ladies and demoiselles shall, for the future, sing nothing but the Psalms of David, and those spiritual melodies which contain the praises of God."

Although no progress toward permanent settlement had been made, Mary Stuart was glad when the session ended. The meeting had awakened her to the realization that François and her uncles were faced with the same internal religious strife in France that her mother had endured in Scotland. She hoped that her uncles would be better able to handle affairs in their own country than they had been in hers.

While they remained at Fontainebleau enjoying the freshness of the woods, the ponds, the gardens, and the hunts, Mary Stuart watched François closely. Though he never complained, she knew he was not well. They were both young and had much to live for. Other kings and queens had surmounted their troubles—she and François could, too.

For a while, after the notables had dispersed, the court remained at Fontainebleau. At last Mary Stuart found for François and herself some of the solitude and peace she had hoped for.

Toward the middle of September the court returned to Saint-Germain-en-Laye, where Mary Stuart gave another audience to the English ambassador, Throckmorton. Ever since the signing of the Treaty of Edinburgh by the Scots and the English, Throckmorton had been urging François and Mary Stuart to ratify it. Each of his visits had been in vain. Now, again, the royal couple declined to comply with his request.

While Mary Stuart enjoyed the early weeks of autumn at Saint-Germain-en-Laye, the Guises were deep in controversy and plans. If the Huguenot party was to be controlled, some of its leaders must be imprisoned, and others executed. The Bourbon Prince de Condé, who had professed his innocence in the Tumult of Amboise and who had fought against his own party, was implicated in another conspiracy on a larger scale. Mary Stuart's uncles were determined that Condé must perish. If he were disposed of and other prominent victims executed at the same time, the Guises might rest secure.

For once the Cardinal and his brother were certain of Catherine de Médicis' willing assistance. She had despised Condé ever since his failure to carry out his part in the Tumult of Amboise. With her, they would prevail upon the King to call a meeting of the General Assembly at Orléans, where the Huguenots were gathered. François must believe that the Assembly was being called to make some definite settlement between the opposing factions and so avert civil war. Condé, his brother, the King of Navarre, and other illustrious Huguenots would be summoned to attend. The Guises would see that the King and Queen were well provided with entertainment and hunting until the Assembly convened; that would leave them free to perfect their own plans. Though the Queen Mother's help would be needed, she must be watched. Spies must look for concealed weapons. The royal troops would surround the city. The Cardinal and the Duc de Guise must be quiet in their movements. This was no time to attract attention or excite suspicion.

Unaware of the real reason for their journey, François

and Mary Stuart set out with the court for Orléans on October tenth, accompanied by twelve hundred horsemen. At Paris the Queen Mother joined the procession. As the royal cortege moved southwards, their party was increased by other Roman Catholic nobles and their soldiers.

Orléans made fitting preparations for the royal arrival. A golden canopy was to be held aloft by the principal citizens. On it were embroidered the arms of the city.

On October eighteenth, François guided his horse under the canopy and proceeded to the Temple of St. Croix. Marching before the King were four hundred archers, two hundred gentlemen of his household, and the arquebusiers of his new guards. Behind rode the King's brother, Prince Charles, with other French nobles.

On crossing one of the richly decorated thoroughfares lined with people shouting *"Vive le Roi,"* François' horse stumbled and nearly threw him. Those who saw it whispered that it was a bad omen not only for the King but also for Orléans.

Undisturbed by the mishap, François with his escort continued amidst clarions and trumpets toward the Temple, where the Bishop waited to welcome him.

Later in the day Mary Stuart, mounted on a white horse and accompanied by the ladies of the court, made her entry into Orléans. Cheer after cheer went up for the young Queen, whose charm and beauty warmed the hearts of the people as it always had.

Unmindful of the tension and secrecy surrounding them, Mary Stuart and François thoroughly enjoyed the lavish hospitality and the hunting parties arranged especially for their pleasure. Meanwhile the Cardinal stayed in seclusion. He spent his time studying maps of the city and of the outlying districts and passageways, planning possible means for escape, listening to reports of his spies, and giving orders. The Duc de Guise waited nearby, watching for false moves from the Huguenots. The Guises must risk nothing. This was a decisive moment in their lives. Their future depended on the success of their plans.

As the first streak of light brightened the sky on October 30, 1560, a single candle flickered in the Cardinal's apartments. The prelate snuffed out the taper, then hurried back to the window. His heart beat faster as he parted the drapery. The sky had grown pinker. The courtyard below was still quiet. There was not a sentinel in sight—that was the way it was intended. The Cardinal wiped a clammy hand on his cassock as he looked across the yard. The hangings were closed in the Queen Mother's chambers. The prelate suddenly grew apprehensive—could Catherine de Médicis be trusted? And then he saw the drapery open at her window. Breathless, he waited. Had his brother, the Duc de Guise, seen—?

The Cardinal flung open his curtain. He tingled with excitement. Royal soldiers crept stealthily into the courtyard. The crouching figures surrounding the enclosure were almost eerie. The prelate's heart beat faster as he pressed his face closer to the pane and gripped the window ledge. He drew back for an instant to wipe the moisture from the glass. It must be kept clear—the Cardinal de Lorraine must not miss a single move of this long-planned event. Condé's capture was worth a hundred executions! The Cardinal held his breath. The door opposite opened as the guards closed in. On tiptoe the jubilant Cardinal strained his neck and eyes to catch a glimpse of his captive, that principal Huguenot leader, the Prince de Condé, as he walked unsuspecting into the midst of the royal soldiers.

Limp with fatigue and excitement the Cardinal clung to

the curtains. The Guises had their first important victim! A tired smile crept across the Cardinal's wan face, as he pictured Condé raging in his prison cell in the custody of four of the Duke's ablest captains of the Guard. Mary Stuart's uncle's smile widened. From his window he could see the King's elated mother, as her broad clasped hands shook joyously over her accomplishment in tricking the Bourbon prince into believing that she was his friend.

As the early days of November slipped by, and the Guises added more Huguenots to their prison lists, the English ambassador at Orléans again pressed the King and Queen to ratify the Treaty of Edinburgh. Throckmorton was aghast as Mary Stuart pointedly replied: "Such answer as the King, my lord and husband, and his council hath made you in that matter might suffice; but, because you shall know I have reason to do as I do, I will tell you what moveth me to refuse to ratify the treaty: my subjects in Scotland do their duty in nothing, nor have they performed one point that belongeth unto them. I am their Queen, and so they call me, but they use me not as such. They have done what pleaseth them; and though I have not many faithful subjects there, yet those few that be on my party were not present when those matters were done, nor at that assembly. I will have them assembled by my authority, and proceed in their doings after the laws of the realm, which they do so much boast of, and keep none of them."

The English ambassador regretted that the ratification of the treaty was refused, as it would give the Queen, his mistress, reason to suspect that no good was intended to her by the King and Queen of France, more particularly as they continued to bear her arms in direct opposition to the articles of that treaty.

"Mine uncles," Mary Stuart retorted, "have sufficiently

answered you on that matter; and for your part, I pray you to do the office of a good minister between us, and you shall do well."

François enthusiastically suggested that they take a short trip to Chambord and Chenonceaux before duties called them back. He knew Mary Stuart loved these châteaux, and both royal residences afforded excellent hunting. Recently the Cardinal had insisted that she and François see more of the Queen Mother and include her in some of their pleasurable activities. Perhaps her mother-in-law would like to join them! Mary Stuart suggested it to François.

Happily the royal family looked forward to this special event. The Queen Mother, Mary Stuart thought, was as eager as her son and daughter. But their joy was short lived. On Sunday, November seventeenth, the day before they were to leave, François had a violent chill. Before the Guises could get him to his bed, the King was flushed with fever and complained of sharp pains in his ear.

Several days later Mary Stuart watched the door close behind the Queen Mother and the court physicians. The physicians' words haunted her. François' condition was worse. They would do their utmost to save him.

Terror gripped the Queen as she listened to her uncles' hurried whispers. The King's condition was concealed from the people. The gates were closed at once. None but Mary Stuart, the Queen Mother, the Guises, and those servants in attendance were to be admitted to the royal chambers. It was a protection for all of them as well as for the Roman Catholic party. Her uncles would do everything possible to save the King. They would bring other physicians.

As Mary Stuart sat helpless at the bedside of her feverish husband, fear and pity mingled in her heart. Her lips quivered, but she bit them. This was no time for tears.

François needed her strength now more than ever. She
would nurse him back to health. François *must* get well!
Life was only beginning for them. She would not leave
the King until he was up—then they would go to their lovely
beautiful Chenonceaux as they had planned. She would
play her lute for him. She would sing all the melodies he
loved. They would dance, be gay, happy, and they would ...

François opened his eyes. Eagerly Mary Stuart leaned
forward. She forced a smile and waited for the parched
lips to speak. But there was only a vacant stare and
François' eyes closed again.

While Mary Stuart, pale and thin, kept watch over her
husband, the Guises paced their apartments nearby. The
King was dying. Their power would go with him. What
might have saved their position was an heir to the French
throne. How fervently each uncle had prayed for this
happy event! But now, at the pinnacle of their power, the
Guises were falling faster than they had climbed.

For, with the passing of François II would come the
accession of his younger brother Charles. There was no
doubt in the Guises' minds that then the Queen Mother
would become Regent of France in fact, as well as in
name. She, who had favored the Huguenots, would not
execute the captive Prince de Condé. Nor would she make
any other move that might deprive her of the power she
would acquire. It seemed almost incredible, yet the
Cardinal and the Duke realized that François' death would
give Catherine de Médicis the power his life had given to
them.

Meanwhile the Queen Mother sat before her writing
table, quill in hand, much pleased with herself. She had
just had a successful secret interview with the Bourbon
King of Navarre. Her courier was on his way with a

dispatch recalling the Constable de Montmorency. The Queen Regent would need Montmorency's military prowess if the Guises should try to take over Charles' government. Even while François hovered between life and death, her thoughts were on her second son, nine-year-old Charles. The Queen Mother would see that, as Charles IX, he would be a credit to his father Henri II and the house of Medici. François would soon be gone. The Queen Mother smiled. Mary Stuart would no longer be Queen of France. Catherine de Médicis would again have precedence at the French Court. The Queen Mother slipped her quill into its holder. It seemed ironic that soon Catherine de Médicis would be the power behind the French throne.

The efforts to keep the King's condition from his court and subjects had only tended to exaggerate the stories that spread from the very day François was stricken. Some believed that the King's illness was only a device of the Guises to keep François from knowing their treacherous dealings with the Bourbon Prince de Condé. Others said their King had been poisoned by a Huguenot attendant. Still others alleged that one of François' barbers had poured a deadly potion into his ear while trimming his majesty's hair. And many clung to the prophetic dream of one of the ladies-in-waiting, "how, on the morning of the fatal tourney at which Henri II was slain, a splinter of the lance of Montgomery had likewise struck the Dauphin in the ear, which stretched him dead."

On December fifth, the eighteenth day of the King's illness, it was announced that François II could live but a few hours longer.

With the Queen Mother, her uncles, and the court physicians, Mary Stuart sat quietly beside her dying husband. There was no thought of crowns, position or what the future held, but only that her seventeen-year-old François whom she had learned to love and appreciate would soon be gone forever!

Toward midnight on December 5, 1560, three days before her eighteenth birthday, Mary Stuart became a widow.

Chapter Seventeen

Mary Stuart shielded her eyes as the hangings were slowly opened to let the daylight in for the first time in forty days. During this mourning period the Scottish Queen had been secluded in her chambers. She had grown used to this semidarkness with only lighted tapers to cast ghostly shadows over the heavy black furnishings and drawn window draperies. How oddly the all-white costume of a royal widow of France contrasted with these doleful hangings!

For the first fifteen days Mary Stuart had seen no one but the young King Charles, his mother, the King of Navarre, the Constable de Montmorency, and her uncles. Then, as the days crept by, she gave audience to a few courtiers and some of the higher clergy, who paid their respects and offered condolences. Then the ministers and ambassadors were admitted. All came except the English envoy, Throckmorton, who had no instructions from Elizabeth to do so.

Filled with pity for the young Scottish Queen, the Venetian ambassador wrote:

"So by degrees everyone will forget the death of the late King except the young Queen, his widow, who being no less noble minded than beautiful and graceful in appearance, the thoughts of widowhood at so early an age, and of the loss of a consort who was so great a King and who so dearly loved her, and also that she is dispossessed of the crown of France, with little hope of recovering that of Scotland, which is her sole patrimony and dower, so afflict her that she will not receive any consolation, but, brooding over her disasters with constant tears and passionate and doleful lamentations, she universally inspires great pity."

For her uncles Mary Stuart had great compassion. How crushed the Cardinal's and the Duke's pride must have been when they had surrendered François' Great Seal to be solemnly broken in the presence of King Charles and his mother! The Cardinal was deeply humiliated when the General Assembly, convened seven days after François' death, formally deprived him of his office as spokesman for the Three Estates. The Queen Mother had realized her great ambition to be vested with the powers of a Queen Regent, and the King of Navarre had now become the first governor of the realm.

Mary Stuart felt no regret when she gave the crown jewels to the Queen Mother to hold in safekeeping for King Charles. But, during the long confining hours of required French mourning, Mary Stuart had much time to consider her future. Now that François was gone, the Guises deprived of their power, and Catherine de Médicis showing open disdain for her, Mary Stuart realized that her days at the French court were numbered. Although the Lords of the Congregation controlled her realm, she knew the time was at hand when she must plan her return to Scotland. It would take some time to settle her affairs in France and make arrangements for her home-coming. Meanwhile she must not jeopardize her future. Mary Stuart loved France. It would not be easy to break away after nearly thirteen years, even though she was still Scotland's Queen!

The passing of François had robbed the Guises of their destiny, but they knew that another marriage for their niece might salvage their lost position. Before Mary Stuart's mourning was over, her uncles were engaged in arranging a second marriage for her with the heir apparent of Spain, Don Carlos, son of Philip II by his first wife, Maria of Portugal. Not only would such a Roman Catholic match give the Guises a new lease on power, it might help bring about the strengthening of Roman Catholicism in Scotland, Ireland, England, and even France.

When the Queen Mother learned of the Guises' negotiations, she did her utmost to prevent them. Secretly she offered the hand of her youngest daughter, seven-year-old Marguerite, to Don Carlos. Catherine de Médicis was aware that if Mary Stuart became his bride the Guises would regain enough power to annihilate her own political authority as Regent.

On hearing of the plans for the Scottish Queen, the English ambassador, Throckmorton, was quick to write the Lords of the Council:

"Among others, the ambassador of Spain hath been with her alone an hour together, which is thought to be far more than the ceremony of condolence required. He hath also since that time dined and had great conference with the Cardinal de Lorraine; and though I cannot yet think that it be about any matter of marriage for her with the Prince of Spain (for I think the council of Spain too wise to think upon it, without other commodity), yet it is not amiss to harken to the matter. For she, using herself as she beginneth, will make herself to be beloved, and to lack no good offers.

"And for my part I see her behavior to be such, and her wisdom and kingly modesty so great, in that she

thinketh herself not too wise, but is content to be ruled
by good counsel and wise men (which is a great virtue
in a Prince or Princess, and which argueth a great judgment and wisdom in her), that by their means she cannot do amiss, and I cannot but fear her proceedings with
the time, if any means be left and offered her to take
advantage by."

Toward the end of January, 1561, her forty days of
mourning over, Mary Stuart moved to a small château
near Orléans. Here she began preparations for her return
to Scotland. A delegation of four Scottish gentlemen was
dispatched to her native land to urge the Scottish Estates
to renew the old alliance with France. She made known
to her parliament her decision to return to Scotland. She
hoped for their love and affection, and she pledged for-
giveness for past offenses. Meanwhile she requested that a
delegation be sent to her with information concerning the
state of affairs in her kingdom.

Charles, accompanied by his mother, Princess Marguerite, and Prince Edouard Alexandre, was a frequent
visitor at Mary Stuart's new residence. The Queen Mother
had long ago recognized her son's love for the Scottish
Queen and Mary Stuart's fondness for him. But Charles
must never come under her influence, or must he ever
wed his brother's widow. That, Catherine de Médicis
knew, would restore the Guises to power.

While Mary Stuart continued to further her personal
plans, and comfort herself with the company of her Lady
Marys, Janet Sinclair, and John Kemp, other suitors were
contending for her hand. However, the Scottish Queen
and her uncles had far more to gain from a Spanish
matrimonial alliance.

In February Mary Stuart moved with the court to

Fontainebleau to be present when Elizabeth Tudor's special envoy, the Earl of Bedford, arrived. The Earl brought congratulatory messages to Charles upon his accession, as well as condolences for Mary Stuart. Elizabeth Tudor's emissary was secretly instructed to do his utmost to prevent a Spanish or Austrian marriage for Mary Stuart. For this purpose he was to enlist the support of the Protestant leaders. It was the English Queen's hope that Mary Stuart would marry a Scot or at least someone who could give her neither political nor financial support.

Mary Stuart received the Earl of Bedford and England's ambassador, Throckmorton, on February sixteenth in the presence of the Duc de Guise, several French bishops, and some of her ladies and gentlemen. When the Earl had presented Elizabeth Tudor's letters and condolences, the Scottish Queen answered in a mournful voice that she thanked the Queen for her gentleness in comforting her woe when she had most need of it; and considering that the Queen now showed the part of a good sister, whereof she had great need, she would endeavor to be even with her in goodwill.

While at Fontainebleau the Earl of Bedford and Ambassador Throckmorton had requested two more audiences with Mary Stuart. At each visit Elizabeth's representatives besought the Scottish Queen to ratify the Treaty of Edinburgh. Mary Stuart asked to be excused, explaining that she could do nothing, as she was without advisors. The Cardinal was absent and none of the Scottish nobility was available. "And I pray you so tell the Queen my good sister," Mary Stuart told the envoys, "I trust ere it be long some of the nobility and Council of Scotland will be here, for I do hear they mean to send some shortly unto me— peradventure you know it as well as I; and when I shall have communed with them I mind to send my good sister, the Queen your mistress, such an answer as I trust she shall be pleased with it; for I mean to send one of mine own unto her ere it be long: in the mean time I pray you, declare unto her from me that I would we might speak together, and then I trust we should satisfy each other much better than we can do now by messages and ministers. This the Queen my sister may assure herself of, that she shall find none more willing to embrace her friendship and amity than I, and there is none who ought to take more place with her than I. Tell her, I pray you, how much I am desirous to see her, and also that I am in good hope it will come to pass."

The day that the Earl of Bedford was to leave the French court he and Throckmorton were granted a private audience with the Bourbon King of Navarre. When the subject of Mary Stuart's second marriage rose, Throckmorton remarked that it was rumored that the Scottish Queen would either marry the Spanish Prince or the Duke of Austria. Either marriage, he stated emphatically, would be of great inconvenience to English interests, and could not possibly make things any easier for the Huguenot King of Navarre. The Bourbon King told Elizabeth's envoys that it was not with the Prince of Spain but with the Austrian Duke that the marriage negotiations were being considered. He was certain of this because he knew the Emperor's ambassadors' visit to the Cardinal de Lorraine could have been for no other purpose. The King of Navarre was concerned. But when Throckmorton pointed out that if Mary Stuart remained at the French court she could be watched and no such alliance could be negotiated without the King of Navarre knowing it, the Bourbon King took heart. He assured the envoys that he would try

to delay, if not prevent, the Queen of Scots' moving to
Joinville, so near the German States, where the Guises
might carry out their plans in secret.

Mary Stuart remained with the court at Fontainebleau
far later than she had planned. And for this delay Bedford
claimed credit in his dispatches to England.

But as March slipped by, the Scottish Queen finally
made ready to leave Fontainebleau for Reims, and then
Joinville. The day of her departure she walked alone
through the garden—the same garden in which she had sat
with her mother nearly ten years before, and with her
François only six months earlier. She was leaving it, but
the cherished memories it held she could never leave behind—her mother's tender smile, her courage at her departure from her daughter, and François' joy in the peace
and solitude they both had found in this enchanted spot.

Mary Stuart had been gone from the French court but a
short while, when the Danish ambassador arrived to negotiate a marriage between her and his King, Frederick II.
Like so many others', his journey was made in vain. The
Guises and Mary Stuart could only think of the Spanish
alliance. Failing that, the Duke of Austria might be considered.

On March twentieth, Mary Stuart, on her way to Joinville, reached Paris. Here she spent the day selecting the
garments and jewels from her costly wardrobe that she
would take back to Scotland. When her choice was made
she proceeded at once to Reims, to the Abbey of Saint-
Pierre-les-Dames.

Upon arriving with her retinue, Mary Stuart was welcomed by her uncles and other kinsmen, among whom was
her grandmother, the Dowager Duchess of Guise. Joyously
the girl embraced her aging grandparent. The hours spent

with her would be cherished. For a moment Mary Stuart wished that she again could be the wide-eyed five-year-old girl who had been held close in her grandmother's arms thirteen years ago. How complex and worrisome her life had grown in the years since then! It was a heavy burden that fate had given her.

During all the years in France her grandmother had given Mary Stuart the mother's love she had so needed. Diane de Poitiers, too, had freely given her affection at all times. Mary Stuart would have liked to see Diane de Poitiers again before she left France, but she dared not further arouse Catherine de Médicis' animosity. She would write Diane de Poitiers, instead.

The French court was filled with speculation at Mary Stuart's sudden move from Fontainebleau. There were rumors that she needed change of air. A gayer atmosphere might help alleviate the grief that still weighed heavily upon her. Others talked of Queen Catherine's enmity toward her daughter-in-law. Some were inclined to believe that the foremost reason was the numerous marriage proposals that had come to the Guises' niece. England's ambassador was worried. The Guises could negotiate freely and secretly for their niece's hand, once they were away from the court.

The English ambassador's agitation mounted when he learned that not only Frederick II, Denmark's king, but also Eric XIV of Sweden, and the widowed Duke of Ferrara were seeking Mary Stuart's hand, and that a matrimonial alliance for the Scottish Queen was being negotiated with either young Charles or Ferdinand, sons of Emperor Ferdinand I. On the arrival of the Duchesse d'Arschot at Reims, Elizabeth Tudor's ambassador surmised at once that the royal lady had not come just to pay her respects, but also to seek Mary Stuart's hand for her wealthy brother, the Prince of Orange.

While the Guises and their niece received the representatives of all these royal suitors, they were careful not to commit themselves. Each contender was sent away hopeful, while the Guises and Mary Stuart waited and hoped that the Spanish alliance would materialize.

Toward the end of the second week in April, Mary Stuart left Reims to visit her grandmother at Joinville and to confer on the way with two Scottish deputies of rival factions. At the village of Vitry, on April fourteenth, she met John Lesley. The future Bishop of Ross brought assurance of the fealty of the Roman Catholics of northern Scotland and advised Mary Stuart to return by way of Aberdeen. Here she would be met by the Roman Catholic nobles who, with an added twenty thousand devoted Roman Catholics, would escort her triumphantly into Edinburgh. The spokesman of Mary Stuart's party then talked of his sovereign's half-brother, James Stuart. Scotland and its Queen would be far safer if she had her half-brother seized and imprisoned in France. Lord James, he warned, had become not only the most powerful and influential, but also the most ruthless leader in the Protestant party. Mary Stuart listened intently and courteously, but did not commit herself.

On April fifteenth the Scottish Queen found her half-brother at St. Dizier. Lord James had come as the representative of the Lords of the Congregation. He proposed that his sister refrain from any interference with religious conditions in her realm. It would be wise for Mary Stuart to return by way of Leith.

The Scottish Queen could not accept his suggestions. She tried in vain to persuade Lord James to forsake the Protestant party and to refuse any further support from

Elizabeth Tudor. Even an offer of a Cardinal's hat, rich abbeys, and excellent benefices did not dissuade her brother. She would try appeasement, then, for the moment. She would appoint him acting Regent for her until she returned to Scotland. If she could not win him over before he left France, she would withdraw her appointment by the time he reached Scotland. Mary Stuart weighed her brother's oath of fealty to her as she left St. Dizier with him to continue her journey to Joinville.

Mary Stuart enjoyed every minute of the short time she spent at her grandmother's home. It was almost like having her mother back again. Her grandmother lived and talked of her own daughter's girlhood as they walked the same paths that the Dowager Duchess had traveled with Mary of Guise when she was nearly Mary Stuart's age. She saw again with poignant interest her mother's favorite trees, shrubbery, and flowers, and special haunts. The Dowager Duchess talked repeatedly of Mary Stuart's likeness to her mother in personality and great devotion to her Church. In her kind and affectionate manner the elderly woman tried to help her granddaughter face the future. She was aware that Mary Stuart's road would not be a smooth one, even if she could duplicate her mother's courage and integrity, and her fidelity to her religion.

After a week at Joinville, Mary Stuart took leave of her half-brother several miles outside of the town. Escorted by her uncles and a select retinue, the Queen of Scots journeyed to Nancy to enjoy the hospitality of her former playmate, Princess Claude, and her youthful husband Charles, Duc de Lorraine. At Nancy, booming cannons from the city walls welcomed Mary Stuart. A gala reception awaited her at the palatial home of the Duc and Duchesse de Lorraine.

Meanwhile, in Spain, Philip II had been considering a

marriage between his son, Don Carlos, and the Queen of Scots. It had many advantages, but they were far outweighed by Catherine de Médicis' threats that she would ally herself with the Huguenots, and by Elizabeth of England's continued enmity toward the Scottish Queen. Spain was not ready to engage in a war with England to keep Mary Stuart on the throne of Scotland. Reluctantly the Spanish monarch told his wife, Mary Stuart's former playmate, Ysabel, to write her mother, Catherine de Médicis, that the marriage negotiations between Don Carlos and the Scottish Queen would proceed no further.

Toward the end of April, while Catherine de Médicis rejoiced over her success in helping to defeat the Spanish alliance, Mary Stuart listened mournfully as her disappointed uncles told of Philip's refusal. Not only would her marriage to the Spanish prince have helped reinstate Catholicism in Scotland, but also it might have prevented France's following the English example of becoming Protestant. Such a marriage would have kept Scotland's young Queen on the continent near her relatives and the people she loved and really knew. Her uncles' power, Mary Stuart realized, was now lost. Catherine de Médicis had triumphed over the House of Guise. Mary Stuart must make her final arrangements for returning to her own country.

Plagued with uncertainty about her future and disappointed by the failure of the Spanish negotiations, Mary Stuart was stricken with a high fever. The Dowager Duchess of Guise hurried to bring Mary Stuart back to Joinville. Here she could look after her granddaughter and keep her free from the English ambassador's constant harassment to sign the Treaty of Edinburgh. Mary Stuart must regain her strength. If the Scottish Queen could not uphold the House of Guise in France, she must avail herself of the opportunity that awaited her in Scotland.

Chapter Eighteen

Mary Stuart had planned to be present at Charles IX's coronation on May fifteenth, but her slow convalescence did not permit it. Toward the end of May, Mary Stuart's grandmother and the young Queen finally bade each other farewell at what each knew was to be their last visit together in France—perhaps their last, ever.

As her retinue left Joinville to return to Reims, Mary Stuart did not look back. Her mother, dauntless and undismayed, had left this same château to journey to Scotland; like her mother, Mary Stuart must go forward fearlessly.

At Reims the Scottish Queen divided her time between her beloved friends at the Abbey Saint Pierre-les-Dames and her uncles. Long hours were spent in serious conferences with the Cardinal and the Duc de Guise. Complicated and important affairs of state and religious matters were discussed. Although Mary Stuart had recognized that the political power of the Guises was no more, it was comforting to have her uncles' personal loyalty and confidence in her destiny.

During the second week in June the young Scottish Queen left her peaceful surroundings. A short distance from Paris an escort of both Huguenot and Roman Catholic nobles met her to conduct her in state through the city where other nobles of lesser rank waited to join the procession. Crowds lined the thoroughfares to cheer their former Queen Consort as she passed by on her way to Saint-Germain-en-Laye to join the King and his mother.

Now that the Spanish marriage negotiations were a closed issue and Mary Stuart had decided to return to Scotland, the Queen Regent could afford to be more kindly disposed toward her daughter-in-law. With young Charles, Catherine de Médicis graciously welcomed Mary Stuart into the royal circle again.

The Scottish Queen was touched by the pomp and ceremony accorded her by Charles IX's court. She was pleased that the King and his mother had chosen Saint-Germain-en-Laye for their sojourn. It was here that Mary Stuart had first met Henri II, Catherine de Médicis, Diane de Poitiers, her uncle the Duc de Guise, and many others. In these palatial chambers she and François had studied together. Mary Stuart could see the Dauphin struggling with his Latin. She could still feel François' hand in hers, as he led her to the dance floor at her first court ball, the one in honor of the Duc de Guise's marriage to Anne d'Este. How delighted the Dauphin had been when all the other dancers had stopped to watch them! Saint-Germain-en-Laye, like lovely Fontainebleau, would soon become another beautiful memory to carry away with her to Scotland.

But before that, there were problems of state to be solved and details for her departure to be arranged. Scarcely had Mary Stuart arrived at Saint-Germain-en-Laye when the English ambassador again tried to obtain her ratification of the Treaty of Edinburgh. The Scottish Queen opened her audience on June eighteenth by declaring that she could do nothing without the advice of the Scottish Estates and the nobles of her own realm. It would be of great offense to her countrymen if she acted without their consent.

"I intend," Mary Stuart informed the ambassador, "to send Monsieur d'Oysel to the Queen your mistress, my good sister, by whom I will give her to understand of my journey into Scotland. I mean to embark at Calais. The King hath lent me certain galleys and ships to convey me home, and I intend to require of my good sister the favors that princes use to do in these cases; I trust that from henceforth we shall accord together as cousins and good neighbors. I mean to retire all the Frenchmen from Scotland who have given jealousy to the Queen my sister, and miscontentment to my subjects. I will leave nothing undone to satisfy all parties—trusting the Queen my good sister will do the like, and from henceforth none of my disobedient subjects shall find aid or support at her hands. But this I assure you," Mary Stuart emphatically told her listener, "I, for my part, am very desirous to have the perfect and assured amity of the Queen my good sister, and I will use all the means I can to give her occasion to think I mean it indeed."

Mary Stuart then proceeded to deal with religious matters, and informed Throckmorton, "You may perceive that I am none of those that will change my religion every year; and, as I told you in the beginning, I mean to constrain none of my subjects, but could wish that they were all as I am; and I trust they shall have no support to constrain me."

It was not long after her audience with Throckmorton that the Scottish Queen's emissary d'Oysel arrived at Elizabeth Tudor's court. He had been charged to request safe conduct for the Scottish Queen and her train in case they were forced by chance to land in England. D'Oysel was instructed to obtain permission for himself to go through England to Scotland so that he could arrange for Mary Stuart's reception upon her return.

On learning of d'Oysel's mission, the English Queen angrily informed him that she could not grant either of his

requests unless Mary Stuart ratified the Treaty of Edinburgh. She advised d'Oysel to return to France with her
reply.

The Scottish Queen's anxiety for news from d'Oysel
brought a slight recurrence of fever. In a dispatch on July
thirteenth, Throckmorton reported the Queen of Scot's illness. Four days later the ambassador was informed that his
sovereign had refused Mary Stuart's requests. He sought
an audience with her at once.

Upon entering Mary Stuart's chambers on July twentieth
at Saint-Germain-en-Laye he found the Queen in conversation with d'Oysel. When she saw the English ambassador
coming toward her, she rose to greet him. Throckmorton
explained that his sovereign did not deem it wise to grant
safe conduct to either Mary Stuart or Monsieur d'Oysel.
He had been commanded to inform her that if she would
be better advised, and agree to the ratification, Elizabeth
would not only grant her passage, but would be glad to
see her in her realm, for her to enjoy the pleasures thereof,
that they might have such friendly conference as might
lead to the establishment of perfect amity between them.

As Throckmorton ceased, Mary Stuart sat and courteously offered him the place beside her. Then she commanded the others to withdraw. With restrained sarcasm
Mary Stuart explained that she was not well and was not
sure that she could control her temper. That being the
case, she would rather not have extra witnesses to her anger
as there had been in England's court when Elizabeth Tudor so rudely refused Mary Stuart's representative the safe
conduct the Queen of Scots requested.

Disdainfully Mary Stuart told the envoy, "There is nothing that doth more grieve me than that I did so forget myself as to require of the Queen your mistress that favor,

which I had no need to ask. I needed no more to make her privy to my journey than she doth me of hers. I may pass well enough home into my realm, I think, without her passport or license, for though the late King your master used all the impeachment he could, both to stay me and to catch me as I came hither, yet you know, Monsieur l'Ambassadeur, I came hither safely; and I may have as good means to help me home again as I had to come hither, if I would employ my friends. You have, Monsieur l'Ambassadeur, oftentimes told me, that the amity between the Queen your mistress and me was very necessary for us both. I have reason now to think that the Queen your mistress is not of that mind; for I am sure, if she were, she would not have refused me thus unkindly. It seemeth she maketh more account of the amity of my disobedient subjects than she doth of me, their Sovereign, who am her equal in degree, though inferior in wisdom and experience— her nighest kinswoman, and next neighbor. I ask her nothing but friendship. I do not trouble her state, nor practice with her subjects; and yet I know there be in her realm those that be inclined enough to hear offers."

Mary Stuart denied that she was at fault regarding the ratification of the treaty. "Mine uncles, being occupied in the affairs of this realm," she said, "do not think meet to advise me in mine affairs. Neither do my subjects, nor the Queen your mistress, think it meet I should be advised by them, but rather by the Council of my own realm. Here are none of them, neither such as is thought meet I should be counseled by."

Regarding her display of England's arms and title, she stated, "I was then under commandment of King Henri my father, and of the late King my lord and husband; and whatsoever was then done by their order and commandments, the same was continued until both their deaths, since which time, you know, I neither bore the arms nor used the title of England. Methinks," she continued, "these my doings might certify the Queen your mistress that that which was done before was done by commandment of them that had power over me."

In an audience with Catherine de Médicis the following day, Throckmorton learned that the Queen Regent approved Mary's refusal to ratify the treaty until she could confer with her countrymen. Catherine de Médicis regretted deeply that her daughter-in-law had not been granted safe conduct by his sovereign. This denial might cause war.

When Throckmorton returned for another audience on July twenty-first, Mary Stuart told him, "If my preparations were not so much advanced as they are, peradventure the Queen your mistress's unkindness might stay my voyage; but now I am determined to adventure the matter, whatsoever come of it. I trust the wind will be so favorable that I shall not come upon the coast of England; and if I do, then, Monsieur l'Ambassadeur, the Queen your mistress will have me in her hands to do her will of me; and if she be so hardhearted as to desire my end, peradventure she may then do her pleasure, and make sacrifice of me—peradventure that casualty might be better for me than to live. In this matter," the Scottish Queen concluded, "God's will be fulfilled."

As Throckmorton took leave of Mary Stuart, his thoughts were not on her repeated refusal to sign the treaty, but on the Queen of Scots herself. She was no longer an affable child, but a woman with ample self-respect and a mature concept of herself as Queen. He sensed the Guises' shrewdness, their tenacity, and the Tudor pride and self-will in Scotland's dauntless Queen. A smile crossed the ambassador's serious face as the door closed behind him. Elizabeth Tudor had a worthy opponent.

Four days later, on July twenty-fifth, Mary Stuart and her aunt, the Duchesse de Guise, rode in the Queen Mother's coach in a brilliant procession. In the cortege headed by Mary Stuart's uncles were King Charles and Prince Edouard Alexandre and a colorful escort of ladies and nobles, including the four Lady Marys, Nurse Sinclair, and John Kemp.

On the outskirts of Saint-Germain-en-Laye the Queen Mother's party alighted. The King and Prince, followed by the ladies and nobles, hurried to Mary Stuart to pay their respects and wish the young Scottish Queen well. As Catherine de Médicis took her daughter-in-law in her arms for a fleeting moment, Mary Stuart was startled to feel the woman's tears moisten her face. Mary Stuart's lips trembled when she embraced the young King, and heard him sob quietly that he would always love her. He had wanted to be with her more, but his mother had interfered—would Mary Stuart forgive him?

Mary Stuart choked. She had long realized that leaving France was not only going from those she had loved and lived with for so long, but forfeiting the joys and the happiness of a country that was part of her life. Gently she released the tearful boy King, and waited while Charles and the royal family departed. Then Mary Stuart beckoned her Lady Marys, Nurse Sinclair, and John Kemp. Together they walked with the Duchesse de Guise to the Cardinal and the Duc de Guise waiting by the litters which would bear the Scottish Queen and her party by slow stages to Calais.

While the young Queen journeyed through Normandy and Picardy, a secretary of the Bourbon King of Navarre had been sent at her request to the English court to ask again for safe conduct. Elizabeth Tudor again refused, unless Mary Stuart ratified the treaty.

Mary Stuart requested a final interview with the English ambassador. At Abbeville on August seventh, Throckmorton answered Mary Stuart's summons, hopeful that by this time she would be frightened enough to agree to his Queen's terms. Again Mary Stuart besought the Englishman to tell her how she might satisfy her cousin Elizabeth.

"By confirming the Treaty of Edinburgh," was the invariable reply.

When Throckmorton departed from Abbeville, Mary Stuart retired to a nearby abbey. Here she hoped to find repose and to be able to quell her despair. Before leaving the abbey she dispatched two more commissioners to the English Queen.

On August tenth Mary Stuart reached Calais. Several large ships and two galleys were anchored in the harbor. The larger one was white, the smaller red, flying two standards—a white flag gleaming like silver in the stern, and aloft a blue one with the arms of France waving gently in the breeze.

The Queen's heart ached. The painted vessels brought back memories. Thirteen years ago almost to the day she had stood with her mother, her four Lady Marys, and Nurse Sinclair wondering at Henri's ships then docked in the Clyde. She had watched the sturdy French crew load her boxes and bales as another staff of French seamen were now loading her furniture, hangings, and other personal belongings. Mary Stuart gazed at the horses she was taking back with her. Would the hills and moors of Scotland offer her the same hunting as the fields and meadows of France?

The Scottish Queen glanced at her four Lady Marys,
grown up like their Queen, and at faithful Nurse Sinclair
and John Kemp. Such loyal friends and servants! Mary
Stuart sighed. Would she find others like them in Scotland
today? She turned to look at her uncles talking to Seigneur
de Brantôme, the court chronicler, her Scottish representative, John Lesley, the French poet Chastelard, and her
former Latin professor, George Buchanan. These gifted
men were returning to Scotland with her. At least she
would have a few of France's learned men at her court.
Listening to their conversation was Anne d'Este, the Duchesse de Guise. How lovely and young her aunt still looked!
The Duc de Guise was as striking and vigorous as the first
day she had met him at Saint-Germain-en-Laye in 1548.
But her uncle, the Cardinal, Mary Stuart thought, had
aged considerably. Both uncles had tried so hard to do
what they thought was right. She could not in this hour of
parting feel anything but love for them both.

Mary Stuart lingered at Calais for five days waiting for
Elizabeth Tudor's reply to her last dispatch. While she tar-
ried, Mary Stuart recalled that she had neglected to present
the English ambassador with the gift that custom ordained
for a foreign prince's envoy. She would have her maître
d'hôtel take the belated token with her apologies to Lady
Throckmorton in Paris.

As a brilliant sun broke through the blue sky over Calais
on the morning of August fourteenth, 1561, Mary Stuart
awakened restless and disturbed. Hurrying into her clothes
she sent for her uncles. She would sail this day, safe conduct or no! Mary Stuart, Queen of Scots, would brave the
voyage as daringly as she had come to France.

Mary Stuart's tight-lipped courage dissolved into a flood

of tears as she flung herself into the outstretched arms of the Cardinal de Lorraine. All the comforting words he offered could not stay the pangs of grief of the Scottish Queen whom he had fathered all these years. With tenderness and a sense of foreboding, Mary Stuart's uncle turned his niece over to Janet Sinclair and John Kemp. Silently he watched the hope of the Guises board the galley. That hope, the Cardinal knew only too well, would soon be out of his reach forever.

The royal galley sailed slowly out to sea with Scotland's Queen remaining on deck for a last glimpse of her beloved France. Unaware of this departure, Elizabeth Tudor finally issued the long-sought safe conduct for Mary Stuart and her entourage.

The order was never needed. Five days later, on August nineteenth, Mary Stuart's voyage came to an end, as the royal ships edged safely into Leith Harbor. While their galley was being moored, Nurse Sinclair helped her mistress into a hooded cloak to protect her from the heavy fog. Then Nurse Sinclair started to move away, but Mary Stuart took her hand and motioned her four Lady Marys and John Kemp to her. Together they had left the shores of Scotland—together they would return to its soil.

With head high, Mary Stuart, the eighteen-year-old Queen of Scots, went forward to face the future.

THE END

Bibliography

BATIFFOL, LOUIS. *The Century of the Renaissance.* New York: G. P. Putnam's Sons, 1916.

BOWEN, MARJORIE. *Mary Queen of Scots, Daughter of Debate.* New York: G. P. Putnam's Sons, 1935.

BRÉGY, KATHERINE. *Queen of Paradox.* Milwaukee: The Bruce Publishing Company, 1950.

BROWN, P. HUME. *History of Scotland.* Vol. II. Cambridge: At the University Press, 1902.

Calendar of State Papers Relating to Scotland and Mary Queen of Scots, 1547-1603. Ed. by Joseph Bain (Vol. I, II). Edinburg and Glasgow, 1898-

CRISS, MILDRED. *Mary Stuart Young Queen of Scots.* New York: Dodd Mead & Co., 1939.

CUST, LIONEL. *Notes on the Authentic Portraits of Mary Queen of Scots.* London: John Murray, 1903.

FLEMING, D. HAY. *Mary Queen of Scots.* London: Hodder and Stoughton, 1897.

GORMAN, HERBERT. *The Scottish Queen.* New York: Farrar & Rinehart, 1932.

HEADLEY, PHINEAS CAMP. *The Life of Mary Queen of Scots.* Boston: Lee and Shepard, 1853.

HENDERSON, T. F. *Mary, Queen of Scots.* New York: Charles Scribner's Sons, 1905.

LANG, ANDREW. *Portraits and Jewels of Mary Stuart.* Glasgow: James MacLehose and Sons, 1906.

MIGNET, F. A. *The History of Mary, Queen of Scots.* London:

Macmillan and Co., Ltd. New York: The Macmillan Company, 1899.

MILLAR, ALEXANDER. *Mary Queen of Scots: Her Life Story.* London: Simpkin, Marshall and Co., 1905. Edinburgh: William Brown, 1905.

M'KERLIE, E. MARIANNE H. *Mary of Guise-Lorraine Queen of Scotland.* London: Sands and Co., 1931.

MONTAIGLON, A. DE. *Latin Themes of Mary Stuart.* London: Richards, 1855.

PETIT, JOSEPH ADOLPH. *A History of Mary Stuart.* London: Longmans, 1874.

POLLEN, JOHN HUNGERFORD. *Mary Stuart.* Edinburgh: T. and H. Constable Ltd., 1922.

READ, CONYERS. *The Tudors: Personalities and Practical Politics in Sixteenth Century England.* New York: Henry Holt and Company, 1936.

STEVENSON, JOSEPH, S. J. *Mary Stuart: A Narrative of the First Eighteen Years of Her Life.* Edinburgh: William Paterson, 1886.

STODDART, JANE T. *The Girlhood of Mary Queen of Scots.* London: Hodder and Stoughton, 1909.

STRICKLAND, AGNES. *Lives of The Queens of Scotland and English Princesses.* Vol. III. Edinburgh and London: William Blackwood and Sons, 1861.
Life of Mary Queen of Scots. London: G. Bell and Sons Ltd., 1913.

SWEIG, STEFAN. *Mary Queen of Scotland and the Isles.* New York: The Viking Press, 1935.

TILLEY, ARTHUR. *Studies in the French Renaissance.* Cambridge: At the University Press, 1922.

TYTLER, PATRICK FRASER, Esq. *History of Scotland.* (Third Edition. Vol. V) Edinburgh: William Tait, 1845.

WEBER, BERNERD CLARKE. *The Youth of Mary Stuart Queen of Scots.* Philadelphia: Dorrance and Company, 1941.

WILLIAMS, H. NOEL. *Henri II: His Court and Times.* New York: Charles Scribner's Sons, 1910.